JANE'S
AVIATION REVIEW

Ashley Biggs

JANE'S AVIATION REVIEW

edited by Michael J. H. Taylor

Fourth year of issue

JANE'S

Copyright © Jane's Publishing Company Limited 1985

First published in the United Kingdom in 1985 by
Jane's Publishing Company Limited
238 City Road, London EC1V 2PU

Distributed in the Philippines and the USA and its
dependencies by
Jane's Publishing Inc,
135 West 50th Street,
New York,
NY 10020

ISBN 0 7106 0333 9

Designed by Bernard Crossland Associates

Printed in the United Kingdom by
Netherwood Dalton & Co Ltd,
Huddersfield, Yorkshire

Contents

The contributors

Michael J. H. Taylor has been a full-time aviation writer for the past 15 years. He began his career by contributing sections to *Jane's All the World's Aircraft*, and remains the compiler of the homebuilt aircraft section. His 50 books range from small spotter's guides for enthusiasts to the five-volume *Jane's Encyclopedia of Aviation*, on which he was editor and major contributor. He has edited *Jane's Aviation Review* since its inception, and his 1984 publications include *Planemakers 4: Shorts* and a history of helicopters.

Don Berliner has been a freelance aviation and science writer for more than 15 years. His specialities include aviation history, sporting aviation and the scientific aspects of unidentified flying objects (UFOs). His output includes more than 200 magazine articles published in a dozen countries, a continuing series of aviation books for teenagers, and a history of world air speed records.

Roy Braybrook is a freelance aviation writer and consultant specialising in military trainers, combat aircraft and guided weapons. His professional experience as a graduate engineer includes air-to-air missile testing in the RAF, and the design and marketing of trainers and V/STOL fighters for British Aerospace (BAe) and its predecessors. Before leaving BAe in 1980 he was technical marketing adviser to the Kingston-Brough Division. He now contributes regularly to numerous aviation and defence journals, and has recently written books on the BAe Harrier and Hawk.

Steve Broadbent spent nine years at British Aerospace Warton, first as an apprentice and then as a flight test engineer on the Jaguar project, before joining *Flight International* in 1974 as avionics editor. Returning to BAe, he worked on the early stages of the AEW Nimrod programme and as an airliner sales executive. In 1980 he moved to a public relations consultancy, where he handled the account of a high-technology client in the aerospace industry. He turned to freelance writing, specialising in aerospace, early in 1983. He joined *Jane's Defence Weekly* as systems editor in 1984.

Austin J. Brown runs the Aviation Picture Library, which specialises in aviation photography for publishers, publicity agencies, manufacturers and airlines. He is also a freelance aircraft captain, having been trained on a course sponsored jointly by Cambrian Airways and the British Government, and has flown aircraft ranging from the DC-3 to the Bandeirante.

Bill Gunston served as a flying instructor in the RAF at the end of the Second World War and in 1951 joined the magazine *Flight International*, being appointed technical editor in 1955. He became a full-time freelance writer in 1970 and has since been responsible for a prodigious output of books, magazine articles and professional reports.

Alan W. Hall trained as a graphic artist and taught in schools of art at Malvern and Stafford before going to the London School of Printing in 1956. Founder editor of *Airfix Magazine* in 1960, he was public relations officer at, successively, the Ministry of Aviation, Heathrow Airport and, for eight years, RAF Farnborough. He started *Aviation News* as publisher/editor in 1972, taking complete control of the business in 1974, and launched *Scale Aircraft Modelling* in 1978.

Bob Hutchinson joined *Jane's Defence Weekly* as news editor in 1983, having spent the previous six years as defence correspondent of the Press Association.

Roy McLeavy was a frequent freelance contributor to the aviation press before launching the magazine *Hovering Craft & Hydrofoil* in 1961. He has been editor and compiler of *Jane's Surface Skimmers* since 1966 and has written several books on advanced marine concepts, one of which has been published in the USSR.

David Mondey AMRAeS, FRHistS, formerly an RAF engineer, has written or edited more than 20 aviation books. Some of the most recent include *Giants in the Sky* and *Milestones of Flight*, co-written with Michael J. H. Taylor, and *Planemakers 2: Westland*.

Kenneth Munson AMRAeS, ARHistS has contributed to *Jane's All the World's Aircraft* since 1968, more recently as assistant editor with responsibility for much of the main aircraft section, sailplanes, microlights, hang-gliders and RPVs. He also has more than 40 books to his name.

J. M. Ramsden FRAeS, CEng joined the aviation weekly *Flight International* after nine years with de Havilland. He was appointed editor of *Flight* in 1964 and is now editor-in-chief. A specialist in air safety, he has won a number of prizes for his work in this area, including the Society of Licensed Aircraft Engineers' Dorothy Spicer Award.

Elfan ap Rees FInstSM, MBIM, AMRAeS has been involved with helicopters throughout his working life. He began his career with the Helicopter Division of the Bristol Aeroplane Company in 1959 and subsequently became a regular contributor to aviation journals, specialising in rotary-wing subjects. In 1977 he launched the magazine *Helicopter International* and today is publisher and editor of that journal and *Helidata*, its associated fortnightly newsletter. He is also a qualified helicopter pilot, an FAI helicopter judge, treasurer of the Helicopter Club of Great Britain, a member of the Rotorcraft Section of the Royal Aeronautical Society, and chairman of the British Rotorcraft Museum management committee. His historical interest in helicopters now extends as far as a personal fleet of 10 vintage autogyros and helicopters.

Norman Rivett runs the APS Photo Library from Biggin Hill, covering aircraft and travel subjects. During his early teens he lived near Croydon Airport, which led to an interest in aircraft and his first job there. Five years in the RAF followed, mostly spent in Malta working on Beaufighters, Meteors and Canberras. After leaving the service he worked in Aden, Saudi Arabia, Iran, Libya and Britain. He has worked as a freelance writer/photographer for the past 25 years.

Martin Streetly BA is a freelance writer and illustrator specialising in airborne electronic warfare. His books include *Confound and Destroy*, a history of the RAF's wartime bomber support group, and *World Electronic Warfare Aircraft*, and he is a regular contributor to *Jane's Defence Weekly*.

John W. R. Taylor FRAeS, FRHistS, FSLAET, AFAIAA began his aviation career in 1941 with Sir Sydney Camm's wartime fighter design team at Hawker Aircraft Ltd. He became a full-time writer in 1955 and has been editor of *Jane's All the World's Aircraft* for the past 25 years. Well over two hundred other aviation books bearing his name have been published, one of them an award-winning history of the RAF Central Flying School.

Reginald Turnill, internationally known writer and broadcaster, was the BBC's aerospace correspondent from 1958 to 1976. He began his writing and reporting career during the 1930s, covering many of the most important aviation events of the period. The launch of Sputnik I in 1957 prompted his specialisation in spaceflight and he is currently editor of and principal contributor to *Jane's Spaceflight Directory*.

Tim Wrixon AMRAeS is aviation editor of *Jane's Defence Weekly*. He has been writing on aeronautical subjects since 1961, when he joined *The Aeroplane* after 10 years as a stressman for Hawker Aircraft at Kingston. He later joined *Flight International*, and from 1970 until the launch of JDW in 1984 was editor of *Aerospace*, the Royal Aeronautical Society's magazine, and in charge of all RAeS publications.

Introduction

This, the fourth *Jane's Aviation Review*, is perhaps more topical in content than any previous edition. Within its pages are covered the launch of a new international airline with a difference, the growing sophistication of surveillance avionics, the Soviet nuclear-powered aircraft carriers currently under construction, and recent events in space. There is also a new-look Jubilees section, which now concentrates on major aircraft company anniversaries, in this case Shorts' 75th and Hughes' 50th.

It is pleasing to record that since 1983 the outlook for commercial aviation has been improving steadily. This situation is best summed up by the results of one major international airline, Lufthansa. For the first quarter of 1984 the German flag carrier reported a 5.4% increase in passengers carried, to 3.36 million from 3.19 million in 1983. Airmail and freight up by 10.7% and 19.9% respectively, were even more impressive. The only blot on an otherwise perfect first quarter was a marginal fall in load factor (seats sold as a percentage of the total offered) from 55.3% in 1983 to 54.8% in 1984. However, seat-kilometres on offer went up by 1.7%, resulting in a net increase in revenue. Encouraged by this performance, Lufthansa ordered two more Boeing 747-200s with side cargo doors, to be delivered in May and June this year.

US military aviation is staging a similar recovery now that the American public is showing itself more willing to listen to arguments for modernisation. There is much to be done, however: Vietnam made it politically very difficult for successive administrations to spend the vast sums needed to keep American equipment, especially strategic weapons, up to Soviet standards. It is not that research and development funds have generally been lacking, but that once the technologies have been developed the money to translate them into operational hardware has not always been forthcoming, or has been blocked for non-military and non-technical reasons. There are many examples of this, including the original B-1, of which 244 examples would otherwise have been operational for the past three years or so. This failure to introduce new systems has given rise to the mistaken belief that the West's forces already operate equipment more advanced than that of the

Heading picture: **Roll-out of the first Rockwell International B-1B strategic bomber from the assembly complex in Palmdale, California, on September 4, 1984.** *(Rockwell International)*

Warsaw Pact. In fact in many fields the opposite is now true. While the West has flaunted its problem-solving ability, it has not followed the Soviet example of making the solutions available in the front line. When the time came for the Soviet Union to complement or replace existing bombers with modern aircraft, for example, no expense was spared in developing and procuring the supersonic variable-geometry Tupolev Backfire and Blackjack. Whenever the Soviet Air Force sees an actual or impending equipment shortcoming, steps are immediately taken to plug the gap. If the resulting system works, there is no question of its not being deployed. Soviet fighters and bombers are therefore designed and built to the highest possible specification and deployed in sufficient numbers, virtually regardless of cost.

The result of this uncompromising approach is an array of high-technology equipment of ever-increasing effectiveness. In the West, by contrast, tight budgets often greatly lengthen development periods, restrict the technology, and force one reduction after another in numbers to be bought. NATO in Europe is currently over-endowed with combat aircraft incapable of full all-weather operation but opposed by superior numbers of all-weather aircraft. Yet even as this is being written the future of the B-1B as a replacement for the USAF's B-52 strategic bombers is finely balanced between limited deployment and cancellation.

The Soviets have a clearer understanding than the public in the West that replacement of obsolete equipment is not arms escalation. The problem of getting this message across has become increasingly difficult in the past few years, a case in point being the NATO decision to deploy tactical nuclear missiles in response to the installation of similar weapons by the Soviet Union. This is perhaps the Alliance's own fault. As an organisation it fails singularly to plead its own case, failing even to exploit such positive moves as the recent voluntary reduction in its stockpile of tactical nuclear weapons to the lowest numerical level since the early 1960s.

This aside, it is now high time for negotiations on nuclear, chemical and space weapons. The last-named area is now growing rapidly in significance. For many years the Soviet Union has conducted test intercepts using killer satellites designed to destroy enemy communications, reconnaissance, tactical targeting, early-warning and navigation satellites in the opening phase of a war. The loss of these facilities would be crippling, possibly decisive. Knowing this, how has the West responded? The USAF has contracted Vought to develop an anti-satellite (ASAT) weapon capable of destroying enemy spacecraft at orbital altitudes. Using a modified SRAM first stage, a Thiokol Altair III solid-propellant second stage, and a Vought miniature

Impression of what was originally designated ISEE-3. Now renamed International Cometary Explorer (ICE), it will be the first spacecraft to meet a comet.

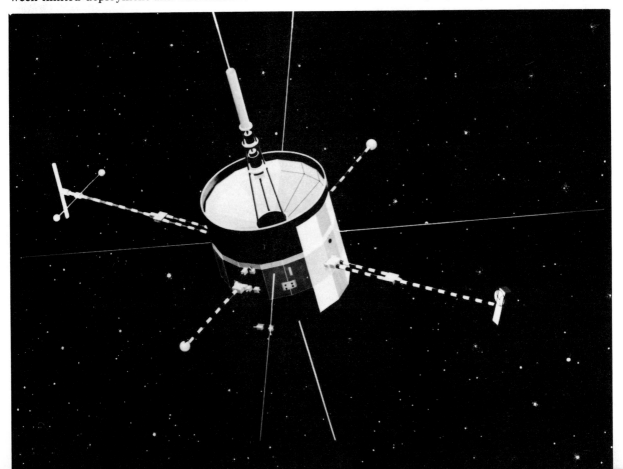

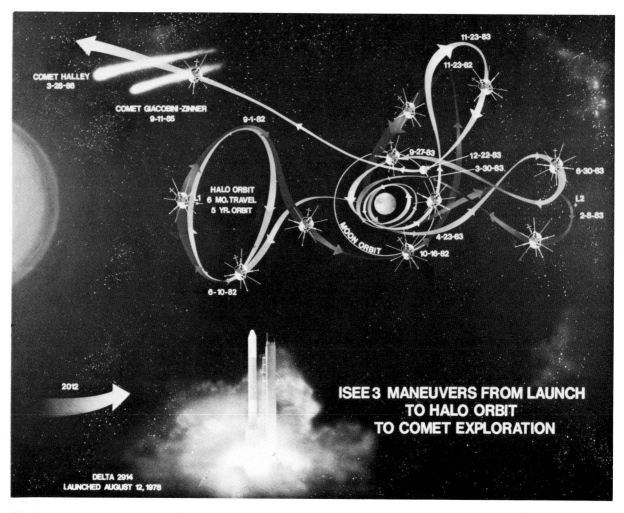

COMET HALLEY
3-28-86

COMET GIACOBINI-ZINNER
9-11-85

9-1-82

11-23-83

11-23-82

HALO ORBIT
6 MO. TRAVEL
5 YR. ORBIT

L1

9-27-83

12-22-83
3-30-83

6-30-83

L2

2-8-83

MOON ORBIT

4-23-83

10-16-82

6-10-82

2012

ISEE 3 MANEUVERS FROM LAUNCH
TO HALO ORBIT
TO COMET EXPLORATION

DELTA 2914
LAUNCHED AUGUST 12, 1978

The International Cometary Explorer's route through space from launch in 1978 to the expected meeting with Comet Giacobini-Zinner and Halley's Comet in 1985 and 1986 respectively.

homing vehicle carrying an infra-red terminal seeker and conventional warhead, it is launched from an F-15 fighter in a zoom climb. However, firing trials only began in 1983, and even if the project escapes cancellation, operational deployment is years away. Moreover, the system's comparatively low altitude capability enables it to attack only certain reconnaissance and tactical targeting satellites, leaving higher-altitude early-warning, communications and navigation satellites invulnerable. Development of a high-altitude anti-satellite system was considered but dropped on cost and arms limitation grounds.

Realisation of the attack satellite threat to the British and French nuclear deterrents has brought about only the slightest reaction in Europe. While there has been talk of using the Tornado F2 as a carrier for a European anti-satellite weapon, words are just about as far as Europe appears prepared to go. Of course the best

outcome would be a treaty to prevent space from becoming just another theatre of war, but until this is achieved it would be very risky to ignore anti-satellite weapons. Equally disquieting is the reported Soviet development of a two-seat mini-shuttle, which could be highly effective in any orbital conflict.

Many people believe that solutions to these problems will be found when the USA and USSR finally discover over the negotiating table how many objectives they actually have in common. The history books may yet record that the 1980s signalled the beginning of a new East-West understanding on the basis of respect rather than fear, and on a realisation that the problems of the Third World outweigh mere superpower rivalry. The use of space for the manufacture of medicines and new materials is of potentially enormous benefit to mankind, but East and West will have to agree on this before either can end space weapon research. The only acceptable close encounters in space should be of the scientific kind. The latest of these is due in September, when NASA's Fairchild-built International Cometary Explorer (ICE) intercepts Comet Giacobini-Zinner some 44 million miles from Earth in the first meeting of a spacecraft and a comet.

Simplicate and lose your shirt

John W. R. Taylor

Bill Stout always reckoned that his greatest contribution to flying was getting Henry Ford interested in building aeroplanes. Without him there would never have been a Ford Trimotor — the famous "Tin Goose" airliner of the 1920s and 1930s — but he is remembered equally for his manipulation of the English language. He told his fellow designers that the key to producing efficient aeroplanes was to "simplicate and add more lightness". It was sound advice. Every pound of unnecessary airframe weight costs money to build and reduces payload and performance in service.

Through the years, engineers have done their best to follow his advice. Back in the mid-1950s Teddy Petter felt that jet fighters were getting altogether too big and heavy. So he designed the Gnat to show that a lightweight fighter could still offer high performance and a heavy punch. Only Finland and India found it adequate as a single-seat fighter, but the Gnat two-seater became the standard advanced trainer in the Royal Air Force and established the reputation of the Red Arrows aerobatic team.

At about the same time, in the Soviet Union, Artem Mikoyan went one better. He showed that it was possible to achieve Mach 2 with an aircraft spanning only 40cm (15½in) more than a Gnat by packing 60% more power into his MiG-21 (known to NATO as Fishbed). In the 28 years since the prototype first flew, MiG-21s have served with more than 35 air forces. After flying one of them in the autumn of 1984 a top US military test pilot said it was the nicest fighter he had ever flown. But Bill Stout's lightness can only be "added" at a price.

The MiG-21 began life woefully short of weapons,

Heading picture: **Last of the "simple" fighters? Northrop's F-20 Tigershark had yet to find a buyer in November 1984.** *(Erik Simonsen)*

fuel and avionics. These shortcomings have been remedied progressively over the years, but there is no way in which a small fighter can ever carry a radar as effective as that in a larger aircraft, or a comparable load and variety of weapons.

All design must therefore be a compromise. This becomes clear when we remember that Artem Mikoyan began work on the MiG-25 Foxbat only a year after the first flight of the MiG-21. The requirement was for a fighter able to intercept the US Air Force's B-70 Val- kyrie Mach 3 strategic bomber at great heights, so Mikoyan was able to forget about lightness, small size and even manoeuvrability. Foxbat ended up at four times the take-off weight of Fishbed. Then the B-70 was abandoned, leaving the Soviet Air Force with an intercepter that was clearly too cumbersome for com- bat with other fighters. But, transformed into an unarmed reconnaissance aircraft, the MiG-25 flies so fast and so high that there is little risk of its ever being shot down.

In contrast, when Arab MiG-21s had to engage Israeli Kfirs, Phantoms, F-15s and F-16s over the Bekaa in Lebanon, they suffered some of the worst maulings in history. Clearly, the limitations imposed by their small size were only one contributory factor, or the Israelis would not be content to make their own next-generation fighter, the Lavi, quite small. More significant is the fact that the Israelis were able to use information from AWACS aircraft to ambush the approaching MiGs, after which heavier firepower and superior pilot skills did the rest.

Problems of a heavyweight

The biggest advantage that Soviet designers appear to have, compared with their Western counterparts, is financial. Their authorities always want the very best aircraft that their engineers can produce, regardless of cost. What happens when government economists insist on budget cuts is illustrated by the sad story of the US Navy's F-14A Tomcat, which ought to be the best fighter in the world.

In theory it should be able to intercept even a MiG-25. Its radar can detect targets up to 315km (195 miles) away; its Phoenix missiles have scored theoretical kills over ranges of 200km (125 miles) when fired against target drones. The trouble is that its TF30 turbofan engines were designed for a different aircraft and were intended originally to power only the first 25 produc- tion Tomcats. Their use in all F-14As was described by US Navy Secretary John F. Lehman in July 1984 as "probably the worst engine-aeroplane mismatch in many years." A US Navy pilot, serving as F-14 prog- ramme co-ordinator, added: "From the very start you essentially teach the pilots to fly the engine as a priority over flying the aeroplane."

To see if things were as bad as they were said to be by Tomcat aircrews, Grumman test pilot Chuck Sewell and Navy pilot Lt-Cdr Bill Baucom undertook what was described as an extremely high-risk programme of

This US Defense Department artist's impression of the two new Soviet advanced-technology counter-air fighters shows a MiG-29 flying over an Su-27 base.

low-altitude, high-angle-of-attack, asymmetric-thrust flights, attaining the kind of attitudes essential in combat against aircraft flying at greater altitude. In 23 flights a total of 254 high-angle-of-attack manoeuvres were performed. They resulted in 54 single-engine stalls and one dual-engine stall.

It takes a brave pilot to fly a 33-ton glider with a maximum wing loading of 642kg/m² (131lb/sq ft), which is why F-14D Tomcats delivered in the late 1980s will have new General Electric F110 engines. Shortcomings in the Tomcat's missiles, too, should have been remedied by then. In July 1984 the US Navy was reported to have refused acceptance of the latest AIM-54C Phoenix missiles because of "marginal workmanship and possible questionable quality control."

During the years when the quality of Western combat aircraft was far superior to that of Warsaw Pact aircraft, it did not matter that NATO air forces were outnumbered 2½ to 1 in Europe. Today, however, the Soviet Union not only maintains the numerical advantage but is closing the technology gap rapidly. New fighters like the MiG-29 Fulcrum and Sukhoi Su-27 Flanker have look-down/shoot-down radars and beyond-visual-range missiles coupled with a speed well above Mach 2 and good manoeuvrability. Western leaders must hope that as the MiG and Sukhoi design

bureaux become increasingly involved in advance technology they too will encounter problems.

Simplication's final fling

Northrop could be the last major manufacturer in the West to try to maintain Bill Stout's concept of "simplication" in its purest form. Having delivered its F-5 fighter family to 31 air forces worldwide, it was willing to pour hundreds of millions of its own dollars into development of a far more formidable — but still small and relatively simple — version which became the F-20 Tigershark. The US Government encouraged the venture as a modern, high-performance export fighter that would not mean sharing the latest US aerospace technology with foreigners. It had no plan to order F-20s for the US Air Force or Navy. As a result, air forces that had been regarded as potential customers began to feel that the F-20 was not good enough for America's own services and was being thrust on them as a "poor man's F-16."

This attitude takes no account of the capability of the beautifully engineered F-20, or of the fact that the aircrew and ground personnel of many foreign air forces would have difficulty in keeping serviceable anything more complex than a MiG-21 or F-20.

Britain's Harrier V/STOL fighter provides another example of how air forces ought to think twice before sacrificing simplicity for other, apparent, advantages. Perhaps few readers will regard the Harrier as simple. Basically, however, its cockpit differs from that of

---

The US Marines' bomb truck: McDonnell Douglas/British Aerospace AV-8B Harrier II, which will be known to the RAF as the Harrier GR5.

conventional attack aircraft only in having an extra lever to rotate its vectored-thrust exhaust nozzles.

In engineering nothing is ever obtained without cost. Critics of the Harrier insist that the price paid for V/STOL capability, in terms of reduced payload/range, is too high. In doing so they overlook the fact that there might not be any runways on which to take off and land conventionally five minutes after the start of any future war. Nor should it be forgotten that in 1982 Harriers were flown with the aid of flight refuelling 12,870km (8,000 miles) from the UK to the Falkland Islands, making only one intermediate stop and landing on a carrier when they arrived. This implies both range capability and ease of handling.

Having learned to appreciate both the attack and air combat potential of the Harriers which they bought from British Aerospace, the US Marine Corps asked

General Dynamics E-7 advanced tactical fighter would draw in additional outside air through wing-root louvres to augment the vertical thrust of its powerplant for hovering. *(NASA)*

Advanced-technology V/STOL version of the F-15 Eagle, being built by McDonnell Douglas, will have foreplanes and vectored-thrust jet nozzles. *(McDonnell Douglas)*

McDonnell Douglas to work in partnership with BAe to produce a new version that would be a genuine "bomb truck" with doubled payload/range. The resulting AV-8B Harrier II gives the Marines what they want, with the help of a more powerful engine, increased fuel, and structural changes which include new wings making extensive use of carbon fibre and other composite materials. These advanced-technology materials save weight, which translates directly into increased weapon load. Unfortunately, the AV-8B is more than 80km/hr (50mph) slower than the RAF Harrier GR3 at sea level, and the RAF learned during the Falklands campaign that every mile per hour is important to survival when attacking a well defended target.

Dozens of different V/STOL techniques have been used in prototype aircraft worldwide. None has approached the efficiency of the relatively simple Harrier, but the search for alternatives continues. To meet US Air Force requirements for a next-generation advanced tactical fighter (ATF), General Dynamics is testing models of its delta-winged E-7 design, using an augmented jet ejector scheme of the kind that has already proved disappointing in the Lockheed XV-4A Hummingbird and Rockwell XFV-12A.

McDonnell Douglas is building an advanced-technology modification of an F-15 Eagle, with movable foreplanes at the front of the engine air intake ducts and jet nozzles which can be deflected downwards to shorten the take-off run. The US Air Force considers this adequate, believing that there will always be strips of roadway or field 460m (1,500ft) long on which to take off between craters. Even if this were true, there are few pilots who would care to land a high-performance jet on a strip that long (or short!), between craters, after a combat sortie.

Doing well by Stealth

Northrop's frustrating experience of trying to sell the F-20 Tigershark could be summed up with the axiom "Simplicate and lose your shirt". Yet Northrop has so much other profitable business that its accountants were able to point smugly to a 61% increase in net income for the third quarter of 1984, compared with the same period of 1983, and a current business backlog of $3.7 billion. Even this is probably only half the story. Northrop's main activity for years to come will be development and eventual production (as prime contractor) of the US Air Force's top-secret Stealth bomber to follow the B-1B in the 1990s. It is highly doubtful that the funds flowing into that programme are shown openly in the financial reports of the companies involved.

"Stealth" is now known officially as "low observability". It covers a wide range of techniques designed to help an aircraft to penetrate defences by eluding detection by radar and infra-red sensors. Lockheed-California has been working on a low-observability fighter for years, and residents in the area of Burbank Airport tell of C-5 Galaxy transports that land by night, pick up well wrapped shapes from the Lockheed factory and whisk them off to a heavily guarded secret airfield in the Nevada desert. The *Baltimore News* has stated that of 14,428 Lockheed employees at Burbank "only several thousand can be explained by unclassified programmes". In October 1984 the newspaper asserted that beginning in 1986-87 between 300 and 400 Lockheed Stealth fighters would be delivered in a programme worth $1.4 billion annually by 1988. On this basis, Northrop's much larger flying-wing bomber ought to replace quite a lot of lost shirts.

Composites, being transparent to radar signals, probably play a large role in the manufacture of Stealth aircraft. But they also raise problems, as helicopter designers have already discovered. They believed that the lightweight strength of the new materials, when used for the complete fuselage and rotor blades of a military helicopter, would greatly increase payload/range performance and make the aircraft almost undetectable in the combat area. NASA has reservations. Its research pilots had penetrated storm clouds more than 700 times, suffering 400 direct lightning strikes on their specially instrumented jet in order to study the effects. They knew already that airliners are struck by lightning more than 2,000 times every year, with little effect, because the aircraft's aluminium skins are natural conductors and their mechanical/hydraulic control systems are immune from the elec-

Sikorsky's S-75, one of two US helicopters built under the Army's Advanced Composite Airframe Programme (ACAP). The anticipated 22% weight saving and 17% cost saving, by comparison with conventional metal airframes, were bettered. *(Sikorsky)*

Above: **One of the many Shorts 360 commuter airliners delivered to US operators.** *(Shorts)*

Below: **Artist's impression of a fully navalised T-45 version of the BAe Hawk trainer landing on a US carrier.**

tromagnetic effects of lightning. But what about aircraft with composite skins, especially if they also use electrical fly-by-wire control systems?

Helicopters are less susceptible to lightning strikes than the higher-flying airliners. On the other hand, if the fuselage of a helicopter made of composites did suffer a strike, the result would probably be a large hole or even disintegration. An obvious answer would be to build a wire mesh into the composite so that the structure would earth itself in much the same way as an airliner. Unfortunately, it would then lose its radar transparency.

The recession recedes

Having been told for years by successive optimistic chancellors that the end of the world economic recession was at last in sight, most of us are now wary of even the most encouraging signs of improvement. However, the 1984 report of the International Air Transport Association (IATA) looked promising. After three years of losses its 134 member airlines achieved a break-even net result after interest and taxation in 1983. An after-interest profit of around $800 million on international scheduled services was predicted for 1984.

Air safety statistics were equally cheering. Worldwide there was not a single passenger fatality on Western-manufactured jet airliners in the first seven months of 1984, during which time the aircraft carried more than 400 million passengers in ten million flying hours.

Boeing, inevitably, was one of the first to benefit from the upswing. A Varig order for two 747-300 Combis carried the total sales of Boeing jet airliners past the 5,000 mark — an average of 172 sold every year since October 1955.

Europe also benefited. Modest contracts raised the order book for BAe's 146 to a total of 41, with 41

options. Shorts of Belfast could report a total of 200 firm orders for and options on their 30-seat 330 and 36-seat 360 by October 1984. Sales resistance had been met initially from airline marketing personnel, who felt that passengers might object to flying in aircraft with such a boxlike shape. But passengers travel *inside* aeroplanes. Once they had experienced the comfort of the 330/360's roomy 1.93m (6ft 4in) square cabin section they tended to feel confined in the circular or oval fuselages of other commuters.

The ultimate mark of approval came with choice of the Shorts Sherpa — a 330 with rear cargo ramp — as the USAF's European Distribution System Aircraft (EDSA). The 18 Sherpas ordered initially are expected to be followed by 48 more, all of which will be used to ferry aircraft spares, including complete engines for the F-15, F-16 and A-10, between Air Force bases in Europe.

The Sherpa is the first British-built aircraft to be bought for the USAF since the Second World War. Its selection came in the year when the US Navy confirmed its choice of the British Aerospace Hawk as its T-45 jet pilot trainer. Contracts worth $438 million have launched a programme that will see some 300 Hawks join the Harrier IIs in joint production by BAe in the UK and McDonnell Douglas in the USA.

More surprising was the decision by Pan American, most American of all airlines, to order a fleet of European Airbuses in a deal involving as many as 91 aircraft worth a total of $1 billion. But such a success for Airbus Industrie should not really surprise anyone. Its member companies — British Aerospace, Aérospatiale of France, MBB of Germany and CASA of Spain — have combined resources greater than those of any

Airbus Industrie lost no time in letting everyone know the name of the latest purchaser of its A310. *(GIFAS)*

other airliner manufacturer, and benefit from nationally funded research by six of the world's greatest aeronautical organisations, starting with the Royal Aircraft Establishment in the UK.

Export orders are of course only one sign of proven excellence in day-to-day operations. Concorde, despite all the criticism once flung at it in ignorance, is now showing healthy operating profits on Atlantic routes and demonstrating to the world that Europe's aerospace manufacturers still retain unrivalled capability in some important fields.

Tornado picks up the prizes
Europe's Tornado combat aircraft is equally impressive. In 1984 the Royal Air Force sent a team of Tornado GR1s from No 617 (Dambusters) Sqn, supported by Victor K2 tankers, to take part in USAF Strategic Air Command's prestigious Prairie Vortex bombing competition. In a field of 42 carefully selected aircrews, and competing against US F-111s and B-52s and Australian F-111s, the Tornados took first and second places in the contest for the Curtis E. LeMay bombing trophy. Although the RAF aircraft had been operational little more than a year, and concentrate almost entirely on low-level flying, the No 1 crew gained 2,616 points out of a possible 2,650 for high and low-level bombing and time control.

No 617 also carried off the John C. Meyer trophy for the F-111 or Tornado crew compiling the highest damage expectancy from its low-level bombing, taking into account evasive tactics using ECM. It was the first time that either trophy had been won by a non-American crew.

Magnificent! But versatile as Tornado may be, only the Soviet Union seems to have produced a flying vehicle that does it all. According to Tass, the Moscow news agency, a Ukrainian amateur designer has built a flying saucer that can be turned into a motor car in a matter of minutes. The vehicle is said to look like an upturned shallow dish with a diameter of 4.88m (16ft). Its chassis has car wheels, and its engine is behind the pilot's seat on a frame of pipes that support a light and durable cupola of duralumin over which special fabric is stretched.

Tass says the device can hit speeds of up to 115km/hr (72mph), lift 100kg (220lb) of freight and "when required, the cupola folds up within a matter of minutes and the flying vehicle is turned into a motorcar which can move along city streets." Unfortunately, no photograph accompanied the story.

Tornado in North America: a high-speed flypast at normal mission height over Niagara.

Farnborough '84

Photographs by Austin J. Brown
Captions by Mark Wagner

Another Farnborough, another show! Not the first words of a song perhaps, but music to the ears of anyone who trades in aviation or who just gets a kick from the sheer noise and atmosphere of a major air event. There weren't many new aircraft, admittedly, but the Soviets made an appearance for the first time, bringing with them the world's largest operational helicopter. Unfortunately, most people had no opportunity to look inside the Antonov An-72, Ilyushin Il-86 and Mil Mi-26, but their presence was certainly a step in the right direction. The one false step of the show was the crash of the DHC Buffalo following one of its customary very steep turning descents. But even then there was comfort to be derived from the obvious strength of the aircraft and the speed with which the engulfing fire was extinguished as the crew walked away suffering from little more than shock. With aircraft from so many countries participating, and with a huge variety of static displays and stands to look over, Farnborough was as Farborough always is — an aviation shop window and a great event.

In hot competition with the Embraer Tucano and the Pilatus PC-9 for selection as the RAF's new basic trainer is the NDN-1T Turbo Firecracker. The Turbo Firecracker can be powered by either a 410kW (550shp) PT6A-25A or a 559kW (750shp) PT6A-25C, and its airframe features a newly designed wing which reproduces certain handling characteristics of jet-engined and delta-winged aircraft.

Heading picture: **Making its international debut at Farnborough with an impressive display was the Pilatus PC-9, which first flew in May 1984. Powered by a Pratt & Whitney Aircraft of Canada PT6A-6B turboprop, it is much more powerful than the closely similar PC-7 Turbo Trainer.**

21

Top: **Embraer and Shorts are offering the Tucano as a contender in the competition to replace the RAF's Jet Provost. Already in service with the air forces of Brazil and Honduras, it will have a split canopy if ordered by the RAF.**

Above: **Hindustan Aeronautics of India chose Farnborough 84 as the venue for the international debut of its HTT-34 side-by-side two-seat trainer, a derivative of the piston-engined HPT-32. Powered by a 313kW (420shp) Allison 250-B17D turboprop and featuring a fixed undercarriage, it is fully aerobatic at its maximum all-up weight.**

Right: **The latest commercial model of the CASA 212 Aviocar, the CASA 212-300 differs from the earlier 200 version in having minor aerodynamic improvements and is powered by two Garrett TPE331-10R turboprops.**

The Hindustan HJT-16 Kiran II is derived from the Kiran 1A, which first flew in 1964. The Kiran II is powered by a Rolls-Royce Orpheus 701 turbojet and features improved avionics and hydraulics.

Left: The first ever Soviet participation at Farnborough caused much excitement. The Antonov An-72 is powered by two Lotarev D-36 turbofans mounted above and forward of the wings to direct exhaust gas over the upper surface of the wings and down over the large multi-slotted flaps. This exploitation of the Coanda effect generates significant increases in lift.

Right: The largest operational helicopter in the world, the Soviet Mi-26 made its first ever appearance in the UK at Farnborough 84. Powered by two 8,500kW (11,400shp) Lotarev D-136 turboshafts driving a unique eight-blade main rotor, it has a maximum payload comparable with that of the Lockheed C-130H Hercules.

Lower right: Canada's contender in the regional airliner stakes is the DHC Dash 8. The Dash 8 fuselage is more streamlined in appearance than those of its stablemates but retains the characteristic T-tail. Powered by two 1,491kW (2,000shp) PWAC PW120 turboprops, the Dash 8 offers a standard passenger seating arrangement of nine four-seat rows.

Below: McDonnell Douglas teamed up with British Aerospace to create the Hawk-based T-45A advanced jet trainer for the US Navy. One of the most obvious external differences between the Hawk and the T-45A is the latter's twin-wheeled nose gear.

Above: **The Airtech CN-235, one of the new generation of regional airliners, is being produced as a joint** venture by Spain and Indonesia. It is powered by two General Electric CT7-7 turboprops.

Prominent wing-root extensions characterise BAe Warton's Active Control Technology (ACT) Jaguar fly-by-wire demonstrator.

Below: **The second of four prototypes of the Embraer EMB.120 Brasilia, Brazil's new regional airliner. Accommodating 30 passengers, it is powered by two 1,118.5kW (1,500shp) PWAC PW115 turboprops.**

Cockpit of the Northrop F-20 Tigershark. Visible in the centre of the coaming and windscreen is the General Electric head-up display, which allows the pilot to keep his attention "out of the cockpit" while selecting and aiming weapons. Piloted by the late Darrell Cornell, the F-20 put on one of the most exciting displays in memory. Cornell was later killed demonstrating the F-20 in Korea.

Left: **British Prime Minister Margaret Thatcher paid a flying visit to the static display. She is seen here in the Edgley Optica aerial surveillance aircraft.**

Below: **On Tuesday September 4 the de Havilland Canada Buffalo demonstrator, piloted by ex-Red Arrow Bill Loverseed, made a very fast landing descent (estimated at 9m/30ft per second) in unfavourable wind conditions, resulting in a heavy touchdown. The wings and propellers were very badly damaged but the fuselage remained intact and the crew were able to walk away unhurt.**

MiGs from the Lone Star State

Michael Taylor

Currently one of the most interesting US military programmes covers the acquisition of supersonic air combat adversary training aircraft for the US Navy. The winning type, General Dynamics' F-16, will enter service in 1987. But losing contender Vought Aero Products continues to believe that its proposal would have been the most realistic adversary of all, and with good reason: the Vought V-601 is none other than the Eastern bloc's classic jet fighter, the MiG-21.

Vought teamed up with Information Management Inc — a company with experience in adversary aircraft maintenance and operation — to offer a fleet of V-601s, newly built MiG-21s supplied by an undisclosed

Heading picture: **Mikoyan MiG-21. This Polish Air Force example carries underwing rocket pods and centreline fuel tank.**

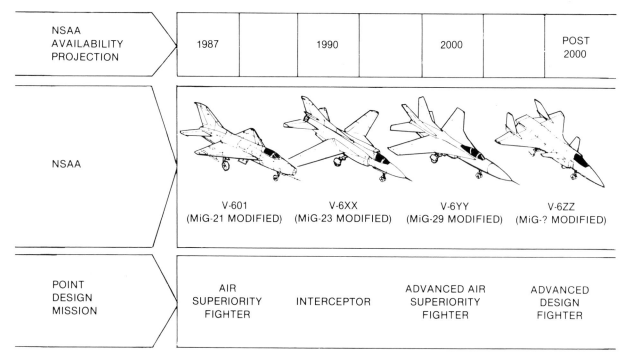

NSAA AVAILABILITY PROJECTION	1987		1990		2000		POST 2000
NSAA	V-601 (MiG-21 MODIFIED)		V-6XX (MiG-23 MODIFIED)		V-6YY (MiG-29 MODIFIED)		V-6ZZ (MiG-? MODIFIED)
POINT DESIGN MISSION	AIR SUPERIORITY FIGHTER		INTERCEPTOR		ADVANCED AIR SUPERIORITY FIGHTER		ADVANCED DESIGN FIGHTER

foreign nation. If selected the MiGs would have been modified to meet the US Navy's requirements for improved communications, navigation and escape systems.

While the MiG-21 is no longer the Soviet Union's most significant fighter, several hundred examples remain in service with Soviet tactical air forces and many more are used by the air arms of more than 30 nations worldwide. Vought believes that "friendly" air combat against real Soviet-designed aircraft would teach Western pilots the art of rapid visual and radar identification of Eastern-bloc warplanes, thereby reducing response times in combat.

Vought is confident that the most advanced Soviet types will ultimately find their way into Western hands. *(LTV)*

Projecting an average utilisation of 35hr per month, Vought expected its V-601s to achieve 90% availability and 80% mission success. The company also saw the Americanised MiG-21 as just the first step in a continuing programme. It expected to be able to offer the V-6XX, a remanufactured/modified late-model MiG-23, by 1990, followed by the V-6YY/MiG-29 at the turn of the century.

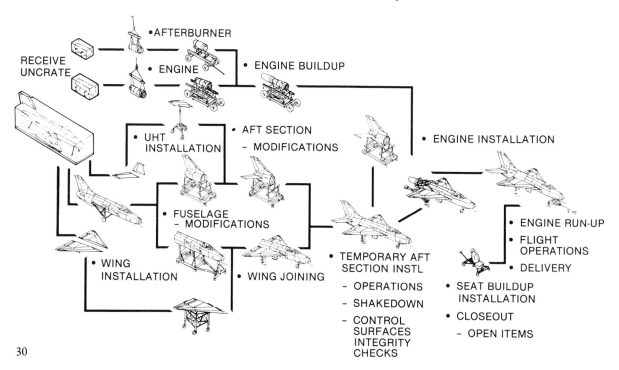

Weatherproof Super Puma

Michael Taylor

Until last year rotary-winged aircraft were severely restricted as to the weather conditions in which they were allowed to operate. Aérospatiale of France has now opened up the helicopter flight envelope by developing its AS.332 Super Puma into the first helicopter to be certificated for all-weather operations, including flight into recognised icing conditions. This clearance applies to the standard AS.332C and lengthened AS.332L civil models. US Federal Aviation Administration (FAA) certification was awarded on 14 March 1984, and similar clearance has been granted by France's Direction Générale de l'Aviation Civile (DGAC).

The FAA and DGAC have also approved the Super Puma for Category II instrument flight rules (IFR) operation. Specified equipment includes a SFIM AFCS 155P autopilot/flight director system and a four-axis SFIM FDC 85 navigation and Category II approach coupler. Super Puma operators can therefore carry out IFR approaches to Category II ILS-equipped airfields. Decision height is 100ft; a missed approach must be initiated if no visual reference has been achieved by the time the aircraft reaches this height. Minimum horizontal visibility is 1,312ft.

Norwegian operators Helikopter Service A/S and AS Lufttransport were the first to order Super Pumas thus equipped. Each aircraft also has de-icing on the main rotor blades and anti-icing on the tail rotor, with a heating mat on the leading edge of every blade; de-iced horizontal stabiliser; icing detector; and nose-mounted weather radar.

Heading picture: **Super Puma operated by AS Lufttransport of Norway.**

Global helo solo

Michael Taylor

At approximately 10.30 am on July 22, 1983, 39-year-old Australian Dick Smith landed JetRanger III *Australian Explorer* at Bell's Fort Worth, Texas, plant to become the first pilot ever to complete a solo helicopter flight around the world. In the course of the 56,742km (35,258-mile) journey, which began on August 5, 1982, Smith had also become the first to fly a helicopter solo across the Atlantic and from the United States to Australia. He also managed to set FAI speed records for London-Darwin and London-Sydney.

With an actual flying time of about 320hr, during which he averaged 177km/hr (110mph) and usually flew at around 150m (500ft) altitude, Smith's epic journey took him to Canada, Greenland, Iceland, the Hebrides, the Scottish mainland, England, France, Italy, Greece, Egypt, Saudi Arabia, Pakistan, India, Burma, Thailand, Singapore, Indonesia, Australia, Indonesia again, the Philippines, Hong Kong, Taiwan, Japan, the Aleutian Islands, Alaska, Canada and the USA. Flying in fog and rain during the North Pacific cros-

sing, he made an arranged refuelling stop aboard a ship because he had been refused permission to land in the USSR.

By carefully planning the journey Smith was able to land on the anniversary of certain historic flights. Jim Mollison's first east-west solo crossing of the North Atlantic in *The Heart's Content* (August 18-19, 1932) was marked by a landing in Scotland on August 19, 1982, at the end of Smith's first stage, between the USA and Britain, and his own solo Atlantic crossing. Smith's final landing of the journey, on July 22, 1983, came exactly 50 years after the American Wiley Post had completed the first round-the-world solo in Lockheed Vega *Winnie Mae*. Taking off on July 15, 1933, Post followed a 25,099km (15,596-mile) route via Germany, the USSR and Alaska, a mere circum-polar effort compared with Smith's truly globe-girdling flight.

Heading picture: **Dick Smith leaves Bell's Fort Worth plant on August 5, 1982, at the start of his epic solo round-the-world flight.** *(Bell)*

Shuttles, space stations and Star Wars

Reginald Turnill

Shuttle Mission 51-A astronaut Joe Allen (left) holds onto the newly retrieved Palapa B2 as Dale Gardner works to attach the adapter used to secure the satellite in its payload bay cradle for return to Earth. This successful demonstration of the astronaut's ability to manhandle large structures in space bodes well for Space Station assembly during the 1990s. *(NASA)*

Right: **In a triumphant vindication of NASA's launch safety procedures,** *Discovery's* **No 2 engine was shut down safely after a 1.7sec burn when the Orbiter's onboard computers detected a No 3 engine ignition failure.** Left: **Mission 41-D finally got under way on August 30, when chief astronaut John Young took this spectacular picture from the Shuttle Training Aircraft.** *(NASA)*

Early setbacks having been overcome, 1984 marked the start of a new East-West space race far surpassing in cost the original race to the Moon which began 30 years ago. The Soviets and the US both have detailed and funded programmes which will keep their space teams fully stretched into the 1990s. Their European counterparts have ambitious programmes too, though not all of them have yet convinced their governments that they deserve to be funded. The space agencies of Japan and India have had no such difficulty, and are pressing on with significant national programmes.

After the success of the first Spacelab mission in November 1983 many expected Shuttle flights to settle down into a routine as reliable as that of a major international airline. Only those aware of the Shuttle's marginal lift-off performance had doubts about NASA's ability to achieve 11 flights in the following year; in the event only five were possible. Observers held their breath when a faulty microchip led to *Discovery's* main engines being shut down after ignition — within four seconds of lift-off and two of SRB firing — and the

maiden flight of the third Orbiter being delayed from June to August. As fire flickered around *Discovery's* tail, launch controllers seriously considered ordering the six crew members — who included Judith Resnik as the second US woman astronaut and Charles Walker, the first non-astronaut passenger — to make a slidewire evacuation. This was not done — it would have meant losing the crew's valuable help with the emergency shutdown procedures — but there was a noticeable lack of ceremony when the crew were hauled out 40min later.

This undignified setback added to the humiliation suffered during February's Shuttle flight, when both Western Union's Westar 6 and Indonesia's Palapa B2 satellites were placed in unusable orbits by the failure of their Payload Assist Module upper stages — an unthinkable disaster in view of the previous perfect performance of the McDonnell Douglas PAM, and a $180 million loss for the insurance market. With the Boeing IUS upper stage, desperately needed for both military and civil use, still out of action, the situation worsened still further in June when another previously reliable upper stage, Centaur, failed to place Intelsat 5-F9 in a usable orbit. With this $102 million loss added to some likely claims for partial failures of earlier Intelsats (the Inmarsat packages have interfered with Intelsat circuits) and a tumbling NOAA-8, the result was to push future insurance premiums above 10%, and in some cases nearer 20%, forcing users back to the days when it was cheaper to carry their own insurance.

Mission 10, or STS 41-B as it was later designated, was redeemed by Bruce McCandless's historic first untethered flight. The Martin Marietta Manned Manoeuvring Unit, which McCandless had helped to develop during most of the 18 years he had waited for his only flight so far, worked perfectly in rehearsals for the recovery of the Solar Maximum satellite on the next mission.

The shock was therefore all the greater when, two months later, it seemed certain that the long-planned recovery and repair of Solar Max had failed. Astronaut George Nelson's MMU took him safely across to the slowly rotating SMM. He then flew deftly between its solar panels but was unable to dock and halt the rotation so that the Orbiter's robot arm could pull the satellite into the payload bay for repairs. At this point NASA desperately needed a success to erase memories of the satellite losses, and, most of all, to prove that the Shuttle was able to retrieve and repair as well as deliver, and was therefore a much more versatile system than Europe's Ariane.

Once again the spirit of innovation displayed by NASA and its contractor engineers and technicians during past crises turned disaster into triumph — with the help of a small miracle when Solar Max, its batteries within 5min of final extinction, turned unaided towards the Sun and picked up enough power to allow the geniuses of Goddard to regain control. Terry Hart's subsequent deft use of the robot arm to recover Solar Max, and its repair and redeployment to resume its solar studies as a perfectly healthy satellite after four years of tumbling, is now a matter of history.

Kennedy Space Centre's launch team, still being rebuilt after the transfer of Rockwell's processing contract to Lockheed, then began the long struggle to get *Discovery* away on its maiden flight. Much else was also happening. Leadership of the $8 billion Space Station, at last given the go-ahead by President Reagan, went to the Johnson Space Centre, with which Kennedy's relations continue to be less than friendly. (JSC regularly sends KSC a list of things that went wrong, with their proposed remedies, following each mission. This infuriates KSC engineers, who have already compiled their own list!) There had to be more cancellations and

First launch of Ariane 3, on August 4, 1984, carrying the ECS-2 European communications satellite and Telecom 1 French national comsat. Following a second successful launch on November 9, the uprated booster is now regarded as fully operational. First flight of the further improved Ariane 4 is scheduled for July 1986. *(ESA)*

postponements of future Shuttle missions while the PAM problems were studied, and the flight to recover the Westar 6 and Palapa B2 satellites from their useless 300 × 1,200km orbits could not be finalised until September because of funding problems. Astronauts Dale Gardner and Joe Allen had to start rehearsing this complicated and hazardous recovery mission long before it was finally agreed that ownership of the two Hughes HS 276 satellites, if they were recovered, would pass to the insurers, who would then give Hughes the job of refurbishing and reselling them. Their successful retrieval in November on Mission 14 (51-A), brilliantly executed by Gardner and Allen with the help of Anna Fisher operating the robot arm, brought much relief to NASA and the recovery of about $50 million-worth of reusable satellites for the insurers.

General James Abrahamson, Space Shuttle Administrator, was transferred at this critical time to become director of the new Strategic Defence Initiatives programme (misleadingly known as "Star Wars") and told that he could spend $26 billion in the next five years on exploring the possible military uses of space. Much of that will in fact be spent on Earth-based investigations of the electromagnetic railguns, pulsed and continuous-wave lasers, advanced tracking and other technologies upon which the proposed four-layered Ballistic Missile Defence system would be based. But since it would require over 500 satellites, there will be plenty of work for the space industry itself.

While some think SDI is an alarming extension of military activities into space, others hold that it is an inevitable response to the Soviets' military space activities, which include an operational anti-satellite (ASAT) system. In the long run there can be no doubt that such a huge injection of money into space research will, for good or ill, result in a quantum leap in man's ability to exploit the fourth dimension.

In the short term these developments have led to a sharp deterioration in relations between NASA and the US Air Force. Having stated publicly that it has little interest in the Space Station (its low equatorial orbit is of little military use and also makes it highly vulnerable), the USAF is insisting that it must order 10 new expendable launch vehicles (ELV) for use at the rate of two per year to ensure that accidental or terrorist damage to the Shuttle or its launchpads does not overnight deprive the military of access to space. The casual intrusion of small aircraft into the airspace around the Cape Canaveral launchpads was highlighted once more when *Discovery*'s first launch was held for 7min while a Piper Aztec was chased out of the area by an unarmed military aircraft. Armed patrols are now being consid-

Shuttle flight log (as at January 1984)

Flight	Launch date Orbiter	Crew	Duration	Details
STS-1	12.04.81 102	Young, Crippen	02.06.21	Near-perfect flight
STS-2	12.11.81 102	Engle, Truly	02.06.13	5-day mission halved by fuel cell fault
STS-3	22.03.82 102	Lousma, Fullerton	08.00.05	Extra day because of storm at Northrup landing strip
STS-4	27.07.82 102	Mattingly, Hartsfield	07.01.10	1st concrete landing. SRBs lost, DoD package failed
STS-5	11.11.82 102	Brand, Overmyer, Allen, Lenoir	05.02.14	1st operational flight; SBS-3, Anik C3 deployed; EVA failed
STS-6	05.04.83 099	Weitz, Bobko, Peterson, Musgrave	05.00.23	Delayed 3 months by engine leaks, etc. TDRS-1, 1st EVA
STS-7	18.06.83 099	Crippen, Hauck, Fabian, Ride, Thagard	06.02.24	1st US woman; 1st satellite retrieval; Anik C2, Palapa B
STS-8	30.08.83 099	Truly, Brandenstein, Bluford, Gardner, Thornton	06.00.07	1st night launch/landing; Insat B

Note Cancellations of STS-10 and 12, and other delays, led to new flight designation system: 1st figure = FY; 2nd fig = KSC(1) or VAFB(2); final letter = sequence.

| STS-9 41-A | 28.11.83 102 | Young, Shaw, Garriott, Parker, Lichtenberg (PS), Merbold (PS) | 10.07.47 | Spacelab 1; 3yr late. Science 90% successful |

Flight No Designation	Launch date Orbiter	Crew	Duration	Details
10 41-B	03.02.84 099	Brand, Gibson, McNair, McCandless, Stewart	07.23.17	1st MMU flights. Westar 6 and Palapa B2 lost. SMM rehearsal
11 41-C	04.04.84 099	Crippen, Scobee, Nelson, van Hoften, Hart	06.23.40	LDEF. SMM repair. 1st orbital retrieval and repair
12 41-D	30.08.84 103	Hartsfield, Coats, Resnik, Hawley, Mullane, C. Walker	06.00.56	SBS-4, Leasat 1, Telstar 3C. Large solar panel. 1st commercial PS
41-E	Cancelled 099	Mattingly, Shriver, Onizuka, Buchli, USAF PS	—	2nd cancellation due to IUS failure
41-F	Cancelled 103	Bobko, Williams, Seddon, Hoffman, Griggs	—	Mission merged with 41-D. Crew reassigned to 51-E
13 41-G	05.10.84 099	Crippen, McBride, Sullivan, Ride, Leestma, Garneau, Scully-Power	08.05.23	OSTA-3, ERBS, LFC. 1st 7-person crew. 1st US female EVA
14 51-A	08.11.84 103	Hauck, D. Walker, A. Fisher, Gardner, Allen	07.23.44	Anik D2, Leasat 1. Recovered Palapa B2 and Westar 6
15 51-C	24.01.85 103	Mattingly, Shriver, Onizuka, Buchli, Payton (USAF)	03.00.26	1st dedicated DoD mission; included 1st military PS. IUS used to launch signal-intelligence satellite
16 51-E	03.03.85 099	Bobko, Williams, Seddon, Hoffman, Griggs, Baudry (France), Garn		TDRS-2, Telesat 8
17 51-D	19.03.85 103	Brandenstein, Creighton, Lucid, Fabian, Nagel, Jarvis (Hughes)		Syncom 4-3. LDEF retrieval
18 51-B	30.04.85 099	Overmyer, Gregory, Lind, Thagard, Thornton, Van den Berg, Wang		Spacelab 3
19 51-G	30.05.85 103	Engle, Covey, van Hoften, Lounge, W. Fisher		Spartan 1, Telstar 3D, Arabsat A, Morelos A

Shuttle Orbiter designations: 099 *Challenger*, 102 *Columbia*, 103 *Discovery*, 104 *Atlantis*.

ered because of the danger of a terrorist attack being carried out in this way when the Shuttle is at its most vulnerable. At first sight this might all seem reasonable, but the whole justification for the US Space Shuttle lay in the fact that it would be relatively cheap because it would replace all ELVs for both civil and military launches. The new USAF policy threatens the final destruction of NASA's fading hopes that cheapness can be achieved by frequent, routine flights. Spread over the planned 11 flights in the 1984 financial year, the Shuttle budget would have meant an average of $287.8 million per flight; with only five flights the average more than doubled. Even if the planned yearly average of 24 is achieved by 1989, it might still prove difficult to get mission costs down to $100 million.

Not that there is any question of the military making no use at all of the Shuttle. It will be a vital research tool for the SDI team. Before Boeing's modified IUS is at last used to orbit TDRS-2 — two years late — the USAF needs to employ the Shuttle/IUS combination on a secret mission to get SDI research started.

All the technical, economic and political pressures which are making things difficult for NASA's Shuttle team must make life seem all the purer, scientifically speaking, for the Space Station Task Force, led by John Hodge in Washington and Neil Hutchinson at

Houston. The main US contractors are already sharing $6 million-worth of study contracts. The current plan is for five modules to be orbited by Shuttle at monthly intervals, starting with a power unit at the end of 1991. Six to eight astronauts would occupy 4 habitable modules, and the $8 billion funding would include two free-flying platforms. One would accompany the station in its 300km/28° orbit, the other, which would be Shuttle-serviced, would be in a 98° Sun-synchronous polar orbit for Earth atmosphere and resources studies.

Two aspects of technology likely to find a place on the Space Station were put through their paces on Shuttle mission 41-D. The McDonnell Douglas electrophoresis system right, seen here being tended by industrial astronaut Charles Walker, is the forerunner of an automatic production plant to be installed aboard the free-flying platform that will accompany the Station.

This "Power Tower" arrangement was chosen by NASA as the configuration on which all Space Station design bids should be based. Key features include, from the bottom, Shuttle Orbiter service vehicle; cylindrical pressurised modules housing workspace and crew quarters; boom-mounted rectangular radiators; large deployable dish antenna; L-shaped remote manipulator arm; box-shaped "hangars" for satellite launch preparation and refurbishment; large folding solar arrays; and ring-shaped spacecraft cradles. (NASA)

Below: This 102-ft long solar array, extended from *Discovery's* payload bay several times during the mission, was used to demonstrate the practicability of the very large panels that will be needed to supply the Station's energy demands. (NASA)

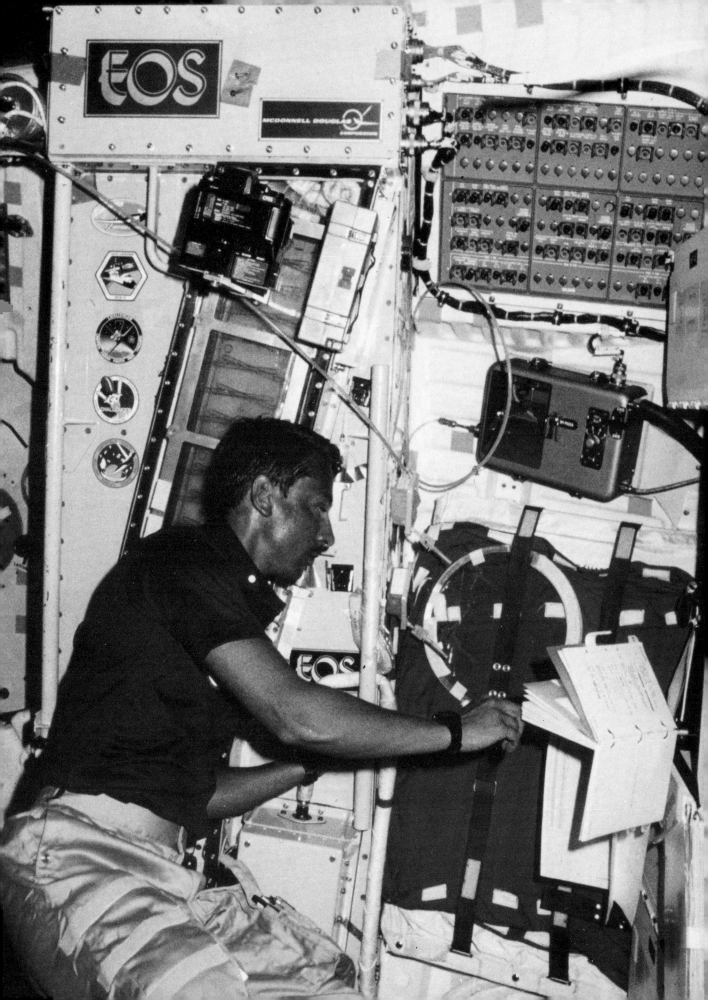

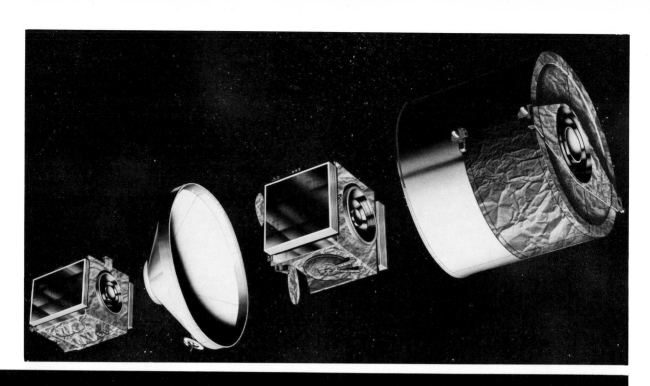

Left: **BAe Dynamics is designing the Satellite Transfer Vehicle under contract from Scott Science and Technology, the company founded by Apollo astronaut David Scott. Launched in the Shuttle payload bay, STV could ferry two spacecraft weighing a total of 8,000lb from low Earth orbit to geosynchronous transfer orbit.** *(BAe Dynamics)*

Below left: **BAe proposal for an unmanned platform to operate in conjunction with the US Space Station. A number of Spacelab-style pallets accommodating payloads from several different users could be berthed on the central beam. The platform would supply the payloads with power, cooling, data-handling and orbital control.** *(BAe Dynamics)*

Below: **Powered by both air-breathing and rocket engines, BAe's HOTOL unmanned reusable launcher would take off from a runway like a conventional aircraft to place payloads weighing up to seven tonnes in low Earth orbit. This expensive project will certainly require backing from outside Britain, and there is talk of offering it to the USAF as a quick-reacting means of replacing knocked-out military satellites.** *(BAe)*

James Beggs, NASA administrator, says that in addition to commercial activities such as processing materials and vaccines, the Station will be used as a starting point for expeditions to some asteroids and Mars, and ultimately for the establishment of a lunar base.

Beggs' tour of Europe, Japan and Canada to seek international support for these bold concepts — the idea was to obtain contributions worth at least an additional $2 billion — has won cautiously enthusiastic support. Germany's space scientists, determined that their country should lead and dominate Europe in Space Station activities, appear to have convinced both their own government and the European Space Agency that Europe should provide one of the four manned modules, developing it from the German/Italian Columbus project, and an unmanned platform to fly either in formation with the US Space Station or separately in polar orbit. France wants to press on with Hermes, the Ariane-launched mini-shuttle, which could be used to service the Space Station and the free-flying platform.

The European governments, due to meet in Rome at the end of January 1985, were not expected to be daunted by the $1.5 billion development costs spread over eight years. They were however likely to need some convincing that the $1 billion per year running costs after that could be covered in commercial benefits from materials processing.

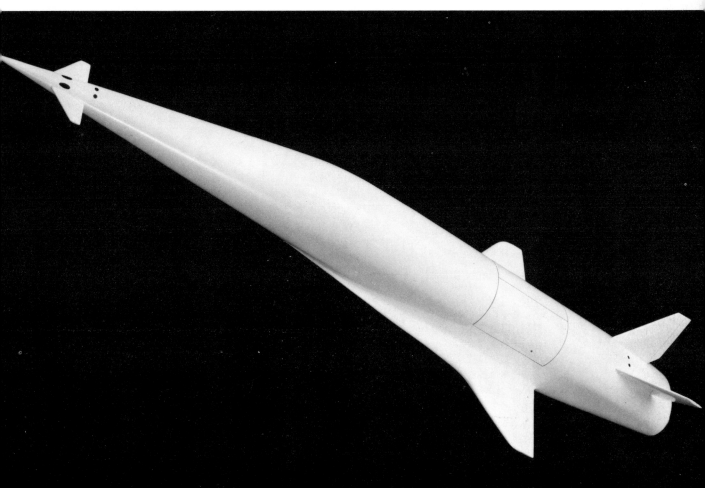

Britain now seems ready to contribute 15-20% of the European budget. But the British Government's hesitant approach at least stimulated British Aerospace Dynamics to propose three major projects to re-establish a more convincing British presence in what is bound to be the main nursery for the new microchip technologies. First came the announcement of a $1 million contract from former astronaut David Scott's Californian-based company Scott Science and Technology for design of a Satellite Transfer Vehicle (STV). Although this faces massive competition from rival projects being developed by companies like McDonnell Douglas and Martin Marietta, it might make an ideal British-led contribution to the Space Station through ESA, and in these early stages is not subject to the usual fatal delays caused by the need to obtain government approval. Next came "Big Communicator," a multi-purpose space platform to be used in clusters to overcome congestion problems in geosynchronous orbits. Finally there was the sensational HOTOL project. This plan for an air-breathing, hydrogen-powered, horizontal take-off and landing unmanned spaceplane caused some initial derision. It would be a long-term project, probably costing at least $3 billion to develop and dwarfing Concorde in complexity. But it is exactly what the USAF needs, and it might suit both Britain and the US if a modest contribution to early design work was made from SDI funds. Neither Britain nor America would now have the Harrier V/STOL aircraft if America had not quietly helped with funding the Bristol-developed vertical take-off engine 20 years ago.

For Soviet space scientists, less subject to national and international constraints, it has been a year of steady progress. America's continuing Shuttle delays provided them with the eagerly sought opportunity to snatch another cherished "first" for the record books — the first EVA by a woman.

As the Soyuz T-10B crew (Leonid Kizim, Vladimir Solovyev and Dr Oleg Atkov), launched in February, patiently worked towards a new long-duration record, they also carried out no fewer than six long EVAs, more than doubling previous Soviet experience in this area. They not only repaired a serious propellant leak, first denied when reported by US sources and then later admitted, but also celebrated their 100th day in orbit by enlarging a solar panel for the second time. Confident that this notable gap in Soviet capability had at last been filled, even those cautious men who dominate Moscow Mission Control could no longer resist the opportunity to send up Svetlana Savitskaya on a second flight to carry out the first female EVA. With only two women cosmonauts available, one of whom had not flown, Savitskaya was the only possible choice. She went up under the leadership of Vladimir Dzhanibekov, only the second Russian to make four flights, aboard Soyuz T-12 in July 1984. He accom-

Svetlana Savitskaya scored another Soviet propaganda point with the first female EVA. She also became the first woman to fly in space twice, just beating America's Sally Ride. More significantly, the Soyuz T-10B flight improved on the Russians' own world record for manned spaceflight endurance.

panied her on the 3h 35min EVA, which was obviously devised for her since she merely tested a bulky welding tool with a 30kg Earth weight and sprayed a silver coating on an aluminium plate. The T-10B crew and Ivor Volk, third member of T-12, gave what assistance was needed from inside. Savitskaya's spacewalk came just a month before Kathryn Sullivan was scheduled to do one for America, though in the event she had to wait until early October, when the seven-person crew of Mission 41-G completed a busy and successful flight.

So, with the passing of Thursday September 6 the Soviets had not only broken their own two-year-old 211-day long-duration record, but had added the first women's EVA and matched US orbital repair capability. The T-10B subsequently went on to record 237 days in space, landing safety on October 2.

Daily satellite monitoring of the Tyuratam launchpads revealed steady progress on a Soviet space shuttle with greater payload capability than America's, plus development of a small quick-reaction spaceplane and two new launchers broadly equivalent to Saturn 5 and Titan. The Soviets therefore appear to be ready to leap ahead of the US in most areas. They should certainly be able to establish a permanently manned space station bigger than that planned by the US, and at least five years before 1992.

When you add to all this the Soviets' fully qualified ASAT systems and the work they are known to have done already on the use of lasers and particle beams in space, it becomes clear that they are poised to win more propaganda victories by demanding, from this position of strength, talks to limit the military uses of space.

With the time fast approaching for the five-satellite onslaught on Halley's Comet, plus Space Telescope and Giotto, it all adds up to an exciting future for those involved in space exploration.

Chronology

June 1, 1983—September 14, 1984

David Mondey

1983

June 1

McAlpine Aviation ordered two BAe Jetstream 31s. They were to be equipped by McAlpine with a multi-role interior capable of quick changes to 8/9-seat corporate, 12/14-seat executive shuttle, air ambulance or freighter configuration.

June 3

Government of Mali ordered a single BAe 146-100, to be delivered before the end of the year.

June 13

The Philippine Air Force announced a $60 million contract for the purchase of 17 Sikorsky S-76 and two S-70A-5 helicopters, for the multi-mission and transport roles respectively.

June 14

First flight of the Beechcraft PD-336 Model 38P Lightning 4/6-seat cabin monoplane prototype, powered by a Garrett TPE331-9 turboprop.

June 20

The first of four de Havilland Canada DHC-8 Dash 8 short-range civil transport prototypes (C-GDNK) made its first flight at Downsview, Ontario, piloted by Robert Fowler.

June 27

The BAe 146 Series 100 and 200 short-range civil transports gained FAA type approval on June 16. Air Wisconsin, which had received its first Series 200 (G-WISC, later N601AW) during the month, introduced the type into service on the route linking Fort Wayne (Indiana) and Chicago O'Hare Airport.

June 27

The Embraer EMB-120 Brasilia regional airliner prototype (PT-XBA) flew for the first time at São Jose dos Campos, São Paulo.

June 29

The first production example of the Armée de l'Air's new two-seat primary/basic trainer, the Aérospatiale Epsilon, was flown at the Aérodrome de Tarbes, Ossun-Lourdes. The first production aircraft were delivered to the Armée de l'Air at Mont-de-Marsan on July 29.

July 1

The Dassault-Breguet Mirage 2000-01 was flown following installation of the 95.1kN (21,385lb st) Snecma M53P2 turbofan. This is the powerplant specified by the Armée de l'Air for its production Mirage 2000 air-superiority fighters.

July 5

The first of the ex-British Airways Lockheed L-1011-500 TriStars entered operational service with the RAF, the inaugural mission carrying 270 members of the 1st Battalion The Gloucestershire Regiment from RAF Brize Norton to Edmonton, Alberta.

July 8

Airbus Industrie A300-600 (F-WZLR), first example of an A300 version with increased passenger/freight capacity (285 passengers maximum), made a 4.5hr first flight.

July 8

The 1,000th production example of the General Dynamics F-16 Fighting Falcon was rolled out at Fort Worth, Texas. Expected total procurement of this air combat fighter was then 2,866 aircraft.

July 20

Westland Helicopters announced an order from the Indian Navy for 12 Sea King Mk 42B ASW helicopters, with an option on an additional eight.

July 22

Australian Dick Smith, flying a Bell JetRanger III, landed at Bell's Fort Worth plant to complete the first solo circumnavigation of the world by helicopter. The flight, covering a total of 56,742km (35,258 miles), had begun on August 5, 1982.

July 25
The first British Aerospace VC10K2 tanker conversion (ZA140) was handed over to the RAF at Filton, Bristol.

July 30
The General Dynamics AFTI/F-16 (Advanced Fighter Technology Integration) aircraft completed a first phase of testing totalling 176 flight hours. Phase II, the operational evaluation, was scheduled to start during 1984 at NASA's Dryden, California, facility.

August 2
Aéromaritime's large-capacity airlift capability was increased by the delivery to Le Bourget Airport, Paris, of its fourth Super Guppy.

August 9
The Mitsubishi T-2CCV (29-5103) made its first flight following conversion as a control-configured vehicle. The aircraft is being used for a two-year research programme by the Japan Air Self-Defence Force.

August 12
Already selected by the UK Ministry of Defence to replace existing installations at RAF airfields, the Plessey Watchman medium-range surveillance and approach control radar was ordered by the Finnish Air Force. The contract covers three complete systems, with an option on four more.

August 17
The Rolls-Royce RB.211-534E4 turbofan, which has been selected to power the Boeing 757 short/medium-range transport, began flight tests in a Boeing 747 testbed.

August 19
The 250th and final Lockheed TriStar commercial airliner, an L-1011-500, was rolled out at Palmdale, California.

August 24
A new world distance record for business jets of 7,023.5km (4,364.2 miles) was set by a Canadair Challenger 601 flying between Calgary, Alberta, and London Heathrow. Flight time was 9hr 4min.

August 29
The first pre-production McDonnell Douglas/British Aerospace AV-8B Harrier II V/STOL close-support aircraft made its first flight at St Louis, Missouri. Total planned procurement is 336 for the US Marine Corps and 60 Harrier GR5s for the RAF.

August 29
The 85%-scale prototype of Beech Aircraft's planned Model 2000 Starship 1, an 8/11-seat business aircraft, was flown for the first time.

September 1
The first NDN Aircraft NDN 1T Turbo Firecracker two-seat turboprop-powered trainer ordered by Specialist Flying Training of Hamble, Hampshire, made its first flight at Sandown, Isle of Wight.

September 3
First flight test of the Westland 30-200. The first of the type to have US-built engines, the -200 is powered by two General Electric CT7-2B turboshafts with a maximum contingency rating of 1,286kW (1,725shp) each.

September 7
Flight tests of the HAL Ajeet Trainer were resumed with the second prototype following a 12-month delay caused by the loss of the first prototype in an accident during 1982.

September 9
The Fuerzas Aéreas Venezolanas received the first of 24 General Dynamics F-16 Fighting Falcons. Delivery of the 18 F-16As and 6 F-16Bs is due to be completed by late this year.

Venezuelan Air Force F-16A (September 9).

September 14

The first production prototype of the MH-53E airborne mine countermeasures version of the Sikorsky Super Stallion was rolled out officially at Stratford, Connecticut. First flown on September 1, this aircraft is being used for a two-year flight test programme.

September 15

Italy's Agusta A129 Mangusta (Mongoose) anti-tank helicopter prototype (MM 590) made its first flight at Cascina Costa, near Milan.

September 29

The official handover of eight Embraer EMB-312 Tucano (Toucan) two-seat basic trainers marked the type's entry into Fôrça Aérea Brasileira service. Six were earmarked for the FAB's aerobatic team, the Esquadrilha da Fumaça.

September 29

Japan Air Lines became launch customer for the Boeing 767-300 254/290-seat transport with an order valued at $560 million for nine aircraft, plus options on a further six.

The crew of Pan American's re-enactment flight stand in front of the silver, blue and white Boeing 707 which retraced the 707 inaugural flight between New York and Le Bourget, France, via Newfoundland (October 26).

Tucano trainers of the Esquadrilha da Fumaça (September 29).

October 11

British Caledonian Airways ordered seven Airbus A320 short/medium-range single-aisle advanced-technology civil transports.

October 26

Pan American commemorated the 25th anniversary of its inauguration of transatlantic services with the Boeing 707 by flying a special service on the New York-Paris route.

October 31
The Panavia Tornado GR1 all-weather multi-role combat aircraft entered service with RAF Germany, equipping No XV Squadron at Laarbruch.

November 1
Birmingham Executive Airways inaugurated a daily Jetstream 31 service between Birmingham and Milan.

November 6
Twenty-fifth anniversary of the entry into Royal Australian Air Force service of the Lockheed C-130 Hercules transport aircraft, marked by an announcement that the fleet had completed 331,000 flight hours without a single major accident.

November 11
The Netherlands Government ordered a further 57 General Dynamics F-16s from Fokker at a total cost of £540.5 million. This will bring the nation's procurement of the type to 213 aircraft.

November 15
Following delivery of the first four of an order for eight Grumman E-2C Hawkeye airborne early-warning aircraft the Japan Air Self-Defence Force established its first AEW unit at Misawa Air Base.

November 16
US carrier Pacific Southwest Airlines ordered 20 BAe 146-200s, valued at £200 million, and took an option on a further 25.

JASDF E-2C Hawkeye (November 15).

November 16
First flight of an advanced version of the Bell AH-1T+ SeaCobra, with two General Electric T700-GE-401 turboshafts and other detail improvements. The US Marine Corps plans to procure at least 44.

November 22
The Egyptian Air Force took delivery of four Dassault-Breguet/Dornier Alpha Jet NGEA light attack aircraft. Also being assembled at Egypt's Helwan factory, these aircraft are expected to replace the MiG-17s currently deployed by the EAF in the close-support role.

November 22
The last three of 24 Sepecat Jaguar Internationals for the Sultan of Oman's Air Force was handed over at Warton, Lancashire. These aircraft equip the SOAF's Nos 8 and 20 Sqns.

November 29
Dornier and the Indian Government concluded a contract covering the licence manufacture of the Dornier 228 by Hindustan Aeronautics.

December 1
The second Northrop F-20 Tigershark prototype (82-0063), which had flown for the first time on August 26, completed a non-stop and unrefuelled flight of 3,714km (2,308 miles) between Edwards AFB, California, and Andrews AFB, Maryland.

December 9
The 1,000th Boeing 737, destined for Delta Air Lines, was rolled out at Renton, Washington.

Pre-production AV-8B Harrier II roll-out (January 12).

December 13
Flight testing of the USAF's Precision Location/Strike System (PLSS), installed in a Lockheed TR-1A, began at Palmdale, California. PLSS is designed to assist in the suppression of enemy detection and guidance radars.

December 15
The first two production Rolls-Royce RB.211-535E4 turbofans for the Model 757 were dispatched to Boeing ahead of schedule. They were installed in an Eastern Air Lines aircraft flown for the first time on February 3, 1984.

December 16
An agreement covering the preliminary design of the Future European Fighter Aircraft (FEFA) was signed by the Chiefs of Staff of the French, German, Italian, Spanish and British air forces.

December 16
A Dornier 128-6 and a Dornier 228-100, named *Polar 1* and *Polar 2* respectively, were handed over to the Alfred-Wegener-Institut for use on the third German Antarctic expedition.

1984
January 9
The initial production example of the Hughes AH-64A Apache anti-armour helicopter was flown for the first time at Mesa, Arizona. The US Army currently requires 515 Apaches.

January 12
The first of 12 pre-production McDonnell Douglas/British Aerospace AV-8B Harrier II V/STOL close-support aircraft for the US Marine Corps was handed over at Cherry Point, North Carolina.

January 16
NATO MRCA Management Agency (NAMMA) placed the last currently planned Tornado order to bring total tri-national production to 805 aircraft. The 157-aircraft batch includes 92 Tornado F2 air-defence aircraft for the RAF.

January 17
The first example of the Boeing 737-300, with an extended fuselage (by 2.64m/8ft 8in) and new engines (two 89kN/20,000lb st CFM56-3 turbofans), was rolled out at Renton, Washington. It flew for the first time on February 24.

January 23
The Sikorsky HH-60D Night Hawk prototype, a conversion of a standard UH-60A, was rolled out at Stratford, Connecticut. First flight was on February 4.

February 14
The first prototype of the Aeritalia/Aermacchi/Embraer AM-X close support and light attack aircraft was rolled out at Caselle, near Turin.

February 15
A training centre for crews of the new Saab-Fairchild 340 twin-turboprop transport was opened at the SAS Flight Academy in Stockholm. The first production Saab-Fairchild 340 was flown for the first time just over three weeks later, on March 5.

February 15
The first T-47A US Navy trainer version of the Cessna Citation II made its first flight. A total of 15 T-47As are currently on order.

February 15
Westland received the go-ahead to build five more Sea King HAS5 helicopters for the Royal Navy in addition to an earlier order for four supplementary Sea King HC4s.

February 24
The US Defence Department announced the selection for the US Air Force of the dual-role McDonnell Douglas F-15E in preference to the General Dynamics F-16XL. Initial plans cover the modification to E standard of 392 existing F-15s.

February 28
The US Army's 158th Assault Support Helicopter Battalion at Fort Campbell, Kentucky, achieved initial operational capability (IOC) with the Boeing Vertol CH-47D. The unit is the first to be equipped with this remanufactured and modernised Chinook variant.

March 1
Almost two years after going bankrupt, US airline Braniff resumed domestic operations. Scheduled routes linking 19 cities were inaugurated with a fleet of 30 of the Boeing 727-200s formerly operated by the airline.

March 2
The US Air Force announced selection of the Shorts 330-200 Sherpa to meet its European Distribution System Aircraft (EDSA) requirement. A £115 million contract covers the supply of 18 aircraft and 10 years' maintenance and support. A further 48 aircraft may be ordered.

March 6
The Airship Industries Skyship 600 20-seat non-rigid airship made its maiden flight at RAE Cardington, Bedfordshire.

March 13
A version of the Gates Learjet 35A for service with the USAF was rolled out at Tucson, Arizona. Initial deliveries of the first of 80 aircraft, designated C-21A, began shortly afterwards. The Learjets are being leased to replace the North American CT-39 Sabreliners used by Military Airlift Command as operational support aircraft.

March 19
The first prototype of the Israel Aircraft Industries IAI 1125 Astra, a more fuel-efficient development of the IAI Westwind, made its maiden flight at Ben Gurion International Airport.

March 27
British Airways inaugurated a thrice-weekly Concorde return service between London Heathrow and Miami,

---

The NASA/US Army Rotor Systems Research Aircraft (RSRA), a modified Sikorsky S-72, made its first flight in fixed-wing, main rotorless form on May 8, 1984. (NASA)

First prototype of the Aeritalia/Embraer AMX light strike aircraft made its first flight on May 15, 1984. It subsequently crashed on June 1, resulting in the death of test pilot Manlio Quarantelli. *(Aeritalia)*

Florida. London-Miami elapsed time, including a 50min stop at Washington DC, is 6hr 35min.

March 27
A Boeing 767 of El Al recorded the type's first non-stop transatlantic flight, between Montreal and Tel Aviv. The 9,334km (5,800-mile) flight took 10hr 52min.

March 28
The first two production Panavia Tornado F2 air-defence fighters were rolled out at Warton, Lancashire. The operational conversion unit (OCU) for this version of the Tornado was due to be formed in September at RAF Coningsby, Lincolnshire.

March 31
The RAF's No 50 Sqn, the last unit to be equipped with the Avro Vulcan, was disbanded at RAF Waddington, Lincolnshire.

April 12
The first Airbus Industrie Airbus A300C4-600, completed in a convertible passenger/freight configuration, was flown at Toulouse.

May 1
No 101 Sqn of the RAF was reformed at Brize Norton to become the service's first VC10 tanker unit. Equipped on formation with four VC10 K2s, it is also to receive five VC10 K3s, with a possibility of more aircraft to follow.

May 22
A Pilatus Britten-Norman BN-2T Turbo Islander equipped to meet the Corps Airborne Stand-off Radar (Castor) requirement formulated by the British Defence Ministry was rolled out at Bembridge, Isle of Wight. It was to be evaluated in competition with a similarly equipped Canberra. The winning submission will be selected for use in the battlefield surveillance role.

May 24
Production of the Dassault-Breguet Atlantic ATL2 updated maritime patrol aircraft was authorised following delays caused by funding difficulties.

May 29
France and Federal Germany agreed to start full-scale development of the MBB/Aérospatiale combat helicopter for the Armée de l'Air and the Heeresflieger.

Mickey Mouse and Donald Duck were on hand when California-based Pacific Southwest Airlines took delivery of its first BAe 146 (May 30). *(BAe)*

Westland Lynx 3 prototype (June 14).

May 30
The first pair of BAe 146s for Pacific Southwest Airlines were handed over.

May 30
The Saab-Fairchild 340 civil transport gained type certification, allowing the initial customer delivery, to Crossair of Switzerland, to be made on June 6. The airline introduced the type on its Basle-Frankfurt and Basle-Paris routes on June 15.

June 2
The uniquely configured Voyager, designed by Burt Rutan, was rolled out at Mojave, California. The 33.78m (110ft 10in) span Voyager has been designed for a non-stop, unrefuelled round-the-world flight in an estimated 12 days. The Voyager flew for the first time on June 22.

June 14
The prototype of the Westland Lynx 3, a new combat helicopter being developed for service in the late 1980s, made its first flight at Yeovil, Somerset.

June 22
Virgin Atlantic began scheduled transatlantic services, between London Gatwick and Newark, New Jersey.

July 2
The first Armée de l'Air Dassault-Breguet Mirage 2000s were declared operational at Dijon-Longvic. The occasion was marked with a demonstration by ten aircraft of the first squadron to use the type, Escadron de Chasse 1/2 *Cigognes*.

July 3
The RAF's first VC10 K3 tanker, a conversion of the civil Super VC10, made its first flight at Filton, Bristol.

July 11
The Indian Air Force received the first three of a planned fleet of 95 Antonov An-32 transports which will replace the Douglas C-47s and Fairchild C-119s currently in service.

Virgin Atlantic's first airliner, a leased Boeing 747 (June 22).

The Agusta A 109A Mk II received British CAA certification in July 1984. *(Agusta)*

July 19
The first production example of the General Dynamics F-16C was handed over to the USAF at Fort Worth, Texas. This advanced version of the Fighting Falcon incorporates many improvements, including a new day/night head-up display (HUD) developed by Marconi Avionics.

July 25
Cosmonaut Svetlana Savitskaya, accompanied by Vladimir Dzhanibekov, became the first woman to make a space walk. Her 3hr 35min EVA was carried out from the Salyut 7/Soyuz T-10B/Soyuz T-12 complex in Earth orbit.

August 1
Two British Aerospace 146-100 transport aircraft were ordered for The Queen's Flight.

August 22
The first production Edgley Optica slow-flying observation aircraft made its maiden flight. At that time some 80 aircraft were on order for service in 25 countries.

The Aérospatiale/Aeritalia ATR 42 short-haul transport flew for the first time on August 16, 1984. First prototype F-WEGA is seen here during ground tests. *(Aeritalia)*

One of the new Spanish CL-215s on a test flight over Lake St Francis. The Spanish Government took delivery of two more of the type and now has the world's largest CL-215 fleet (August 22). *(Canadair)*

August 27
The Grumman X-29A forward-swept wing advanced-technology demonstration aircraft was rolled out at Calverton, Long Island.

September 3
Start of Operation Full Flow, the transfer from the UK to Germany of 57,000 troops and their equipment, 35,000 of them by air. They were due to participate in the Lionheart/Cold Fire exercises, the biggest to involve the British Army and RAF since the Second World War.

September 4
The first production Rockwell International B-1B long-range multi-role strategic bomber was rolled out at Palmdale, California. The event was overshadowed by the loss on August 29 of a B-1A, since attributed to crew error.

September 13
Pan American World Airways announced its intention to acquire 16 Airbus Industrie A320s (plus 34 on option) and 12 A310-300s (13 options) at a total cost of $1,000 million for delivery in 1986-92.

September 14
Lifting off from Carbon, Maine, in the 2,860m^3 (101,000cu ft) helium-filled balloon *Rosie O'Grady*, ex-USAF Colonel Joe Kittinger (well known for his extreme-altitude parachute jumps in 1959-60) set out to attempt the first solo non-stop balloon flight across the North Atlantic. He landed at Savona, Northern Italy, on September 18 to enter the record books once again.

The first production B-1B strategic bomber was rolled out on September 4, 1984. *(Rockwell International)*

Hawk 200:
affordable combat power

Roy Braybrook

The cost of buying and operating combat aircraft in their traditional form has run far ahead of inflation. The result is a downward spiral: the more expensive such aircraft become in real terms, the fewer are purchased and consequently the higher the unit production cost. Unchecked, this trend could have very serious consequences for fighter manufacturers. There is an element of truth in the joke about the Swiss Aviation Corps ending up with one F-15!

In an effort to maintain their numerical strength the world's air forces are turning increasingly to the second-hand market. The attraction of old aircraft is particularly strong in the ground attack sector, since recent progress has largely been confined to nav-attack systems, which can be readily fitted to ageing but otherwise satisfactory airframe-engine combinations. Thus there is active interest in the elderly A-4, while the middle-aged A-7 and Jaguar may enjoy much wider use second-hand than they did when new.

Heading picture: **Mock-up of the Hawk 200, seen for the first time at Farnborough 84.** *(Austin J. Brown)*

Artist's impression of a single-seat Hawk 200 with nose radar, centreline Sea Eagle anti-shipping missile, two Sidewinder air-to-air missiles and two 864lit (190 Imp gal) external tanks. *(British Aerospace)*

The alternative approach is to acquire an operational derivative of one of the jet trainers now in production. Such an aircraft might well cost as much to buy as an updated A-4, but subsequent spending on fuel, servicing and maintenance would be far less. The new type should have a much longer fatigue life, and in certain cases would offer very similar speed and warload-radius performance. In addition, the trainer derivative might also be able to offer limited air-to-air capability at low levels, where even the fastest fighter can exceed Mach 1.0 only by a small margin, and where no aircraft is likely to cruise supersonically for any significant length of time. Finally, commonality with an existing trainer fleet can yield valuable economies.

On published data, the most remarkable aircraft in the trainer derivative category is the British Aerospace Hawk 200, a single-seater shown in mock-up form at Farnborough in 1984 and which should be flying as a prototype at Farnborough in 1986. Although it currently appears that emphasis will be placed on day/night ground attack, using a variety of sensors in combination with an advanced head-up display (HUD) and possibly night-vision goggles, the Hawk 200 will have many other roles.

The adoption of internal cannon frees the centreline store position for other uses such as the carriage of a multi-sensor reconnaissance pod or a sea-skimming anti-ship missile. In the strike and surveillance missions the Hawk benefits from its large internal fuel volume, economical Rolls-Royce Adour turbofan and massive external tanks. The all-aspect attack capability provided by air-to-air missiles such as the AIM-9L tends to reduce the need for high speed in air defence aircraft. The Hawk is therefore genuinely capable of defending a point target like an airfield, having a good prospect of a forward-hemisphere or beam shot against an oncoming attacker.

The Hawk began life as a replacement for the Gnat advanced trainer and the Hunter weapons trainer in RAF service. However, from the outset the intention was to export large numbers of Hawks both as trainers and ground attack aircraft. Early estimates pointed to a world market of around 5,000 aircraft in these categories, with Hawker Siddeley Aviation and Dassault-Breguet anticipating sales of 1,000 units each for the Hawk and Alpha Jet. In order to achieve this operational flexibility, the Hawk airframe was designed with five hardpoints, each capable of carrying a nominal 454kg (1,000lb) store.

The Hawk was the subject of a single fixed-price contract covering R&D and the production of 176 units, of which all but one were to be delivered to the RAF. The resulting T1 is powered by an Adour 151 of

23.13kN (5,200lb) minimum thrust, giving a maximum speed of 1,000km/hr (625mph) in level flight. It weighs 5,035kg (11,100lb) clean and with full internal fuel for take-off in the flying training role. The Hawks operated by the RAF's tactical weapons units (TWU) normally fly with a centreline 30mm Aden gun pod, a 68mm rocket pod under one wing, and a practice bomb carrier under the other. All RAF Hawks have structural (though not electrical) provision for two additional wing pylons, but there is no provision for external fuel.

Some TWU and all the Red Arrow Hawks are being converted to T1A "war role" standard, the eventual total being about 90 aircraft. The original MoD contract included a demand that all RAF Hawks be capable of conversion by contractor's working party to full five-pylon export standard. However, it appears that defence economies have limited both the number of aircraft to be modified and the extent of the modification. In spite of earlier studies aimed at giving the RAF Hawk a ground attack capability (if only as a last-ditch anti-invasion measure), these aircraft will now be restricted to the low-level airfield defence role, armed with the centreline cannon and two AIM-9 Sidewinders on the inboard wing pylons. The sighting system will be the standard Ferranti ISIS used at the TWUs. Reports indicate that each pair of Hawks will be directed to firing positions by a Phantom making use

of its look-down radar. Conversion to T1A standard also includes modifications to rectify earlier faults, such as the introduction of a new UHF radio and standby, and a twin-gyro platform to replace the earlier compass system. In the longer term, all TWU Hawks may be given HUDs and radar altimeters.

The Hawk was first offered for export with the same engine as the RAF aircraft, the Adour 151 being redesignated the 851 for overseas use. In late 1977 Finland signed an order for 50 Hawk Mk 51s, with deliveries beginning in December 1980. The armament system of the Mk 51 differs from that of the T1 in having the Saab RGS-2 gunsight in place of ISIS, ejection release units to take either NATO or Warsaw Pact stores, and a centreline pod that can accept the 12.7mm VKT/42 machine gun in place of the Aden cannon. Most of the Mk 51s are used for training at Pori (No 21 Sqn), but reports indicate that there will be four-aircraft reconnaissance flights at three operational bases, including Rovaniemi (No 11 Sqn) and Rissala (No 31 Sqn). It is believed that these aircraft will carry the Vinten VICON 18 Series 3 camera pod.

The second export order was for 12 Mk 52s for Kenya, or rather an "unspecified African country"

The two-seat Hawk demonstrator with centreline Vinten VICON 18 camera pod, two 864lit (190 Imp gal) tanks and four Sidewinder missiles. *(British Aerospace)*

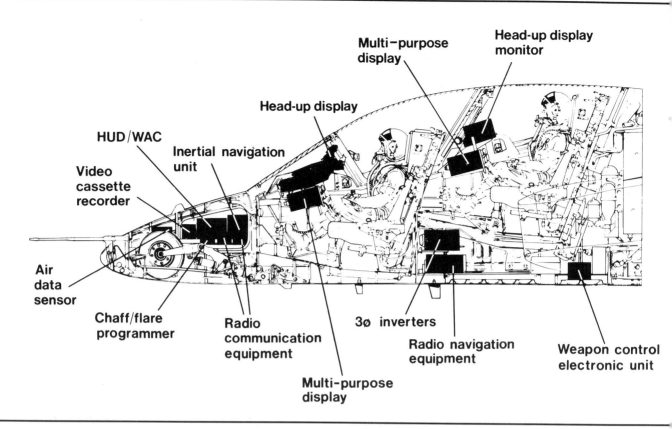

Multi-purpose display

Head-up display monitor

Head-up display

HUD/WAC

Inertial navigation unit

Video cassette recorder

Head-up display

Air data sensor

Chaff/flare programmer

Radio communication equipment

3ø inverters

Radio navigation equipment

Multi-purpose display

Weapon control electronic unit

Location of equipment in the two-seat Hawk Mk 100. *(British Aerospace)*

(which insists on having its aircraft ferried out in Kenyan markings). The Mk 52 differed mainly in having a braking parachute to facilitate landings at the 1,860m (6,100ft) high Laikipia airbase (formerly Nanyuki). It is believed that some African Hawks have been used operationally for ground attack. All export Hawks are suitable for both pilot training and air-to-ground use, with an external store capacity of up to 3,100kg (6,835lb), giving a maximum take-off weight of up to 8,340kg (18,390lb). In this respect the Hawk is the leader of its class by a large margin.

A third 50-series customer was Indonesia, with a current total of 20 Mk 53s on order. These aircraft are employed in the training role at Jogjakarta, replacing T-33s, but in view of Indonesia's insurgency problem it is possible that additional Hawks will be ordered for ground attack use.

Following the first Indonesian contract, BAe decided to switch to the more powerful Adour 861 of 25.35kN (5,700lb) static thrust, Hawks so powered being designated the 60 series. The first order for the series totalled eight Mk 60s for Zimbabwe, with deliveries beginning in 1982. A larger braking parachute was installed to facilitate operations at higher weights, and a fourth flap position was introduced to suit take-offs with heavy loads.

Four of the Mk 60s were attacked by saboteurs at Thornhill airbase on July 25, 1982, when plastic explosive charges and white phosphorus grenades were thrown down their intakes. One was written off, one was repaired in-country, and two were brought back to the UK for repairs.

Later sales in this series consisted of eight Mk 61s for Dubai, 16 Mk 63s for Abu Dhabi (likewise a member of the United Arab Emirates), and 12 Mk 64s for Kuwait. It may be significant that Dubai has subsequently bought four Aermacchi MB-339s, possibly with a view to transferring the Hawks to the ground attack role. The Adour 861-powered Hawk will also serve with the US Navy as the T-45, replacing the T-2 Buckeye and TA-4J Skyhawk from 1990.

Technical developments for the 60 series included refinement of the wing leading-edge devices, giving an extra ½g of maximum turn rate with extremely good control. As an alternative to the Sidewinder for the air-to-air role, the Matra 550 Magic has been cleared for at least one export customer.

For some years the marketing men at BAe Kingston have felt that the Hawk's operational potential could be fully exploited only by introducing a comprehensive nav-attack system. Originally designated Hawk EGA (Enhanced Ground Attack), this concept was first proposed to Venezuela in a mix with the Mk 62 trainer, but the sale was lost as a result of the Falklands conflict of 1982.

Artist's impression of the single-seat Hawk 200 with nose forward-looking infra-red (FLIR), chin-mounted laser ranger and eight 500lb bombs. *(British Aerospace)*

However, BAe persisted with the idea of a ground attack two-seater, which became known as the 100 series. The nav-attack system includes a Singer Kearfott inertial system (as used on the Venezuelan F-16A) and a Smiths HUD. Other changes include hand-on-throttle-and-stick (HOTAS) operation, which groups all vital combat controls and switches on the throttle handle and control column grip. A full range of radio navaids is offered, together with IFF, a radar warning receiver, and laser and forward-looking infra-red (FLIR) equipment.

Compared to the 60 series, the 100 series will be able, thanks to the HUD, to fly safely at lower level, and will navigate and deliver its weapons more accurately. The manufacturer is also considering the introduction of a coloured multi-purpose display (MPD), which would replace two flight instruments and allow other types of information to be shown, including checklists, a moving map, and the TV display of the Hughes AGM-65 Maverick air-to-surface missile. Possible weapon loads include the BAe Sea Eagle anti-shipping missile and various lightweight ASW torpedoes.

The existing two-seat Hawk has impressed many operators with its warload-radius performance, manoeuvrability, tolerance of large and heavy external stores, and high speed. A figure of 1,038km/hr (648mph) at low level has been quoted for the 60-series. Although there are good arguments for having a second crew member in any modern combat aircraft, some air forces refuse to buy two-seaters for this type of applica-

tion. The manufacturer has therefore studied the possibility of a single-seater, which would have advantages in the areas of rear view, nose-mounted sensors and armament. The single external cannon could be replaced by two inside the nose, making the centreline station available for a bomb or missile. A nose radar or other sensors could also be carried.

The single-seat Hawk 200 has 80 per cent airframe commonality with the two-seater. Aircraft systems will be largely unchanged, but gaseous oxygen will be replaced by On-Board Oxygen Generation System (OBOGS). The single-seater is envisaged in two basic forms: the 200-60 based on the operational equipment of the 60 series, and the 200-100 with the far more advanced equipment of the 100 series. Nose sensors are expected to take the form of a laser ranger for daylight operations, FLIR for night, and an advanced radar for all-weather anti-shipping strikes and air defence missions with medium-range missiles. The production Hawk 200 will be powered by the 27.11kN (6,100lb st) Adour 871.

With the large tanks it will be able to remain on station at 185km (115 miles) radius for four hours, armed with two Sidewinders and two cannon. In close support it will deliver 2,720kg (6,000lb) of bombs over a 250km (155-mile) radius in a lo-lo mission. Carrying 2,270kg (5,000lb) of bombs, it can achieve a radius of 1,000km (621 miles) on a mixed-profile interdiction mission. Ship strike radius with one Sea Eagle missile is over 1,480km (920 miles). These are figures that would be respectable enough for a full-scale strike aircraft, let alone a trainer turned mini-fighter.

Bird's eye view of the battlefield

Steve Broadbent

Good soldiers down the ages have used elevated positions to obtain a better view of enemy dispositions, and hills, towers, balloons and aircraft have been turned successively to this purpose. Today technology is rapidly changing the techniques of airborne battlefield surveillance, and there have been major developments in at least five projects in this field during recent months.

For many years it has been common practice to observe the enemy over short ranges using small helicopters, which can operate close to the battle line and direct attacking aircraft by radio. They can take advantage of the cover offered by trees and other natural camouflage, though such protection is limited

by the need to hover high enough to give the observer a clear sight of the target.

It has now become possible to fit an optical sight which passes through the helicopter's rotor mast so that the observer's viewpoint is actually above the rotor blades. This arrangement, known as a roof or mast-mounted sight, enables the helicopter to hover lower, making it much safer from detection and attack. There are several competing designs, notably from McDonnell Douglas (USA), Saab Scania (Sweden), SFIM

Heading picture: **The Lockheed TR-1 is so demanding of its pilots, and flies at such high altitudes, that a pair of two-seat TR-1B trainers have been built.**

(France) and Ferranti (UK), all of which combine a laser rangefinder with the optical sight. The laser can be used either to determine the target's range for transmission to other aircraft, or it can be coupled directly with the helicopter's weapons system for the automatic launch of missiles.

Designing the sights has not been easy. First, the optical and laser paths must be strictly segregated so that there is no reflection of laser light back into the observer's eyes. Second, the observer needs a very stable picture, so the sight must be gyro-stabilised. Finally, the design must be kept as light as possible to minimise impact problems in the event of a crash.

During the past two years the US Army has been testing the sights to assess their suitability for service use. These basically visual systems have been evaluated against electro-optical and other sensors, together with a variety of on-board computers, to determine which mix of sensors gives the required performance. The outcome appears to be victory for McDonnell Douglas,

which has received an initial order for 16 units to be installed in OH-58D scout helicopters. The European manufacturers have however succeeded in selling systems to their own armed forces and, in some cases, to export customers.

But in spite of the advent of roof sights there are a lot of question marks hanging over the use of forward observation helicopters. The extra cover afforded by the use of roof sights is very limited, especially when the tree canopy is uneven or broken, and the latest infra-red missiles and battlefield radars reduce still further the helicopter's ability to conceal itself. The cost and complexity of the sights is also relatively high. A solution to these problems is at hand in the form of the remotely piloted vehicle. RPVs have long been used for many military tasks, but only recently, with the advance of micro-electronics, has it become possible to design a surveillance system which can be incorporated into a small air vehicle in order to acquire comprehensive battlefield information without risking aircrew lives.

The British Phoenix battlefield surveillance RPV, one of the largest programmes yet proposed in the

Hughes 500MD/MMS-TOW with Hughes Aircraft mast-mounted sight. *(Hughes Helicopters)*

The recovery of RPVs intact is all the more necessary now that they carry such high-technology payloads as thermal-imaging cameras and radio links. Here an Israeli Scout is recovered in a net, the method which will also be employed by the UK's Phoenix. *(IAI)*

West, is equipped with an infra-red sensor to give it a round-the-clock capability. Phoenix was the subject of a two-way competition between teams led by Ferranti and GEC Avionics and based on air vehicles developed by Slingsby and Flight Refuelling respectively. GEC emerged as the winner in late 1984, and a production contract was imminent at the time of writing.

Phoenix will fly under remote control just behind and perhaps 600-900m (2,000-3,000ft) above the battle line, relaying information to a centralised control room well protected from attack. The latest technology permits a sensitive thermal imager to be fitted into a very small airframe (a laser rangefinder may well be added later), and the package is stabilised so that the controllers on the ground see a clear, steady picture by day or night and in almost any weather. Each contender has a highly advanced sensor. The Ferranti design has a Rank Pullin imager incorporating a revolutionary coaxial scanning system which eliminates the need for complex, high-precision mirrors. The GEC submission has what is believed to be the first infra-red zoom lens in an RPV.

Phoenix will cruise for 2-3h out to a range of 70km (43.5 miles) from base. The thermal imaging camera will be able to detect a tank at a range of 2km (1.24 miles). It is anticipated that in time a Phoenix Mk 2 would offer an endurance of up to ten hours and a range of 150km (93 miles).

While Phoenix is recoverable and reuseable, and its design concentrates on low noise and radar signatures to minimise the possibility of detection, a high operational loss rate is anticipated. Several hundred systems will therefore be required eventually. The initial contract is expected to be worth some £100 million, but follow-on orders and system development should increase that figure significantly: big business indeed for the winning contender.

There is also significant British interest in an even smaller RPV, and the British Army has ordered ten Ravens from Flight Refuelling for evaluation. Raven weighs only 15kg (33lb) and has a speed of 130km/h (80mph). It is equipped with a conventional day-night television camera, pictures from which are relayed to a ground control station. Smaller still is the ML Sprite helicopter RPV project, which offers a 6km (3.7 mile) range and a speed of 111km/h (69mph). All three British services are said to be interested in this concept. (See also *Letting the drone take the strain*.)

Once the observing vehicle moves more than a few

The Flight Refuelling Raven in flight. This system is being evaluated by the British Army as a complement to Phoenix and Castor. *(Flight Refuelling)*

miles away from or more than a few thousand feet above the battlefield visual and electro-optical surveillance become impractical, particularly in a European environment. The emphasis then changes to radar, the only technology that can sense over ranges much in excess of ten miles.

Two projects, based on the Islander and Canberra respectively, are competing to meet the British forces' Corps Airborne Stand-Off Radar (Castor) requirement. The winning system will operate above Phoenix to complete the battlefield surveillance picture. Phoenix would be launched to investigate in detail any area of interest identified by Castor. The Islander,

equipped with a Ferranti radar in a specially extended nose to permit 360° coverage, was originally conceived by Pilatus Britten-Norman as an airborne early-warning (AEW) platform but has since been adopted by the British Army as a Castor contender. In the meantime, the AEW Islander concept remains alive, being proposed with a Thorn EMI Searchwater radar normally used for maritime surveillance.

The second Castor contender, favoured by the RAF, comprises a Canberra, refurbished by Shorts and equipped with another type of Thorn EMI radar. Both

Pilatus Britten-Norman Islander fitted with a large nose radome to accommodate the Ferranti 360°-scanning radar being proposed by the British Army for the Castor project.

aircraft were being evaluated at the time of writing, with service entry due in 1989, at the same time as Phoenix. While the two Phoenix contenders are very similar in concept, so that the decision was based largely on performance and cost, the Castor proposals differ fundamentally, the Canberra operating at very much higher speeds and altitudes than the Islander-based contender. Politics and inter-service rivalry are therefore likely to loom large in the selection process.

At higher altitudes we come to the most complex part of the surveillance jigsaw. The first Nimrod AEW3 was delivered to RAF Waddington at the end of 1984, and the service will eventually have 11 aircraft operational. The fact that it is eight years since the project was given the go-ahead is a mark of its complexity.

The RAF will eventually deploy a fleet of 11 Nimrod AEW3s for detailed, wide-ranging surveillance of Europe's airspace and land and sea areas. *(BAe)*

Nimrod, together with its NATO partner the Boeing E-3A, will survey the scene from 9,150m (30,000ft) over a 322km (200-mile) radius. The information they gather, whether by active radar or by listening to hostile transmissions, will be relayed to the ground stations of the Improved UK Air Defence Ground Environment (IUKADGE), where it will be processed before being passed on to commanders. Although Nimrod and E-3A are primarily designed to detect other aircraft in the air and ships at sea, they do have capability against land forces.

If AEW Nimrod is the ultimate in airborne surveillance complexity, then the Lockheed TR-1 (and its sister aircraft the U-2R and TR-1A) is the last word in mystery. Now operational with the USAF's 17th Reconnaissance Wing at Alconbury in eastern England, the TR-1 surveys the ground from well over 21,335m (70,000ft) altitude and can stay airborne for ten hours or more. The project started life 30 years ago as the U-2, used extensively in the 1960s and 1970s for high-altitude reconnaissance missions over Eastern-bloc territory. The extensively redesigned TR-1 is deployed for reconnaissance of the forward edge of the battle area (FEBA).

The TR-1 can carry a variety of sensor packages in the ventral and dorsal "Q" bays and in special wing pods. These payloads are easily interchangeable, the most important comprising an advanced synthetic-aperture radar, reconnaissance cameras, and a radar locating system known as Precision Emitter Location Strike System (PLSS), currently in development. Optical systems known to have been used in the aircraft include one capable of high-definition photography over slant ranges in excess of 161km (100 miles), Earth-resources cameras, and cameras which can cover an area of 220km² (85sq miles) from an altitude of 19,800m (65,000ft) with a resolution better than 0.61m (2ft).

The TR-1 series is said to carry several radar systems, though details are sketchy because of the highly secret nature of the aircraft and their deployment. A U-2R has been observed carrying a number of flat dielectric panels (which would make up a sideways-looking radar) together with arrays of electronic intelligence (Elint) aerials, while the TR-1A is reported to have the UPD-X SLAR, which has a range of about 130km (80 miles).

The very advanced electronic and computing technology of the TR-1's synthetic-aperture radar gives it the performance of a system with a very much larger antenna. It is therefore likely that the TR-1s based at Alconbury can detect very small targets on the surface — individual tanks certainly — and transmit a very detailed radar picture to an underground operations room. This radar, again highly classified, is being developed by Hughes Aircraft. Other radar projects, all designed to give detailed coverage of the Earth's surface, have been tested on members of the TR-1 family over the years.

PLSS is currently undergoing trials in the USA and will doubtless be operational in Europe before long. The concept started life in the early 1970s and is believed to have been tested in U-2Cs in Europe before deployment in South-east Asia. Then came four years of development work on the present system, starting in 1977, with some of the trials again being carried out in England.

It is currently planned to equip 10 of the 17th Reconnaissance Wing's TR-1As with PLSS. The aircraft would operate in teams, probably of three, flying racetrack patterns well behind the FEBA and sharing three distinct tasks. One is the detection of enemy radar transmissions; even if an individual transmission was very short, it could be located exactly by means of triangulation data derived from ground-based distance-measuring equipment. Similarly, the position of friendly attacking aircraft and missiles would be continuously monitored, and all data transmitted to a ground controller. Finally, if a missile or air attack was ordered against a specific target, the TR-1s would relay guidance signals from the ground base to the attacker.

Advancing technology is rapidly making detailed airborne surveillance of the battlefield more and more practical at all levels. Thanks to the 'accelerating pace' of electronic development, the days of the "fog of war" could well be numbered.

Can Virgin top the low-fare charts?

Alan Hall

On June 22, 1984, a new airline, Virgin Atlantic, started transatlantic services from London Gatwick to Newark, New Jersey. Offering fares way below those of the regular scheduled carriers, the new operator also represented a challenge to other carriers in the cut-price market and to the non-scheduled charter operators. A one-way ticket to America cost £99, later increased to £110, and a first-class return £1,013. Equipment was a single Boeing 747 leased from the manufacturer.

On the face of it there seems to be nothing remarkable about any of this. First Laker, then other operators such as North West Orient, People Express, Air Florida and World Airways have all tried their luck at the transatlantic cut-price game. So why is Virgin

Heading picture: **Richard Branson, the millionaire owner of Virgin Atlantic, and his daughter Holly seen before the departure of the first service from Gatwick to New York, on June 22, 1984.**

65

different? The answer lies in the nature of the people behind the enterprise. The new airline differs from its predecessors and contemporaries in being born out of the pop music world, which has made one man, Virgin entrepreneur Richard Branson, a millionaire before his 30th birthday.

The Virgin Group was founded 12 years ago. It is privately owned and Branson is the major shareholder. Amongst its assets are a music division, recording studios, a recording label, five nightclubs, 40 retail shops, property and cable TV companies, and interests in film-making, book publishing, computer games and video casettes. Each of these activities is said to making a handsome profit, and the whole appears to be fully capable of supporting a fledgling airline, even one offering services on one of the most cut-throat routes in the world.

Virgin's application for a cheap-fare transatlantic route was made over 12 months before operations started. Final approval came only two days before the first service, but this did nothing to reduce the impact of one of the most spectacular send-offs that Gatwick has ever seen, followed by a flight that few on board will forget in a hurry. In true showbiz style Branson signed up popular artists to travel on the inaugural flight, leavened the mix with media folk like Clement Freud and David Frost, and topped up with plenty of journalists to record the goings-on. Others on the passenger list included Bonnie Langford, Una Stubbs, Katie Rabett and ex-Miss World Mary Stavin. Magician Simon Drake and the singing group Mint Juleps enter-

tained during the flight, and illusionist Uri Geller bent every piece of cutlery in sight.

Maxim of Paris was engaged to provide the in-flight cuisine, being retained on subsequent services for the eight-seat first-class section. Anyone travelling in this exclusive part of the 747's upper deck can look forward to exceptional service, with sleeperette seats, personal steward and private bar coming as standard. For the inaugural flight Guinness provided the only beer on board, and the 300 passengers got through no fewer than 1,000 cans during the 7hr crossing. The entertainment began at take-off with a view on the film screen of the cockpit, the pilots and the runway beyond. However, it turned out to be a cleverly timed spoof, with the "pilots" turning around to reveal themselves as cricket stars Ian Botham and Viv Richards.

But with that memorable maiden flight behind it, Virgin Atlantic has had to get down to the job of selling seats in the face of stiff opposition, and this the company seems to have done with reasonable success. The publicity generated by the first flight helped boost sales during the remainder of the summer season, but since then Virgin has had to survive on its merits.

Virgin's biggest operational problem is its single-aircraft fleet, though another is to be leased as soon as possible. In the meantime, Boeing 747-287B G-VIRG (ex-N354AS) flies a daily service, leaving Gatwick's

Virgin Atlantic's Boeing 747-287B G-VIRG, first aircraft operated by this new and unconventional carrier on the transatlantic route.

satellite terminal at 16.15 every day and arriving at Newark at 18.55 local time. Virgin Atlantic is thus the last of the cheap-fare carriers to depart, the People Express, World, North East and British Caledonian flights having left earlier in the day. The return flight leaves Newark at 21.55 the same day and arrives at Gatwick at 09.35 the following morning.

G-VIRG is a relatively new aircraft, having been built in 1976. It had completed 19,500 flying hours before being acquired by Virgin Atlantic. The company has sub-contracted its maintenance to British Caledonian at Gatwick, and passenger and baggage services to Gatwick Handling. It is not yet known whether Virgin intends to exploit the 747's underfloor

A view of Gatwick's satellite terminal, from which the Virgin Atlantic service to Newark, New Jersey, leaves daily at 1615hr. *(BAA)*

freight capacity, but it can't be long before this profit-conscious company finds some way of turning it to full advantage.

Before entering service with Virgin the 747 was stripped of all interior fitments and remodelled in the red and light grey company colours. Seat pitch is two inches more than the standard in the main cabin and, naturally, a superior audio-visual system has been installed, though passengers still have to pay for the hire of the headsets. Other innovations include new designations for the various cabins within the 747. Unlike most other scheduled operators, which have either one class or a mixture of economy and business, Virgin has tailored its accommodation more closely to passenger needs. Sections A and B (forward) are "quiet zones" — Section B does not even have the in-flight film — while Section C is reserved for families with young children, offering cartoons, U-rated films, popcorn and ice cream. The sections aft of that are standard economy, with unedited films and the usual choice of smoking or non-smoking. Passengers can also buy duty-free goods and tickets for the coach trip from Newark to New York City's World Trade Centre or Grand Central Station. On eastbound flights British Rail tickets are available to passengers going on to London. All flights include in the fare a full four-course meal with wine, and afternoon tea. Baggage allowance is 20kg per passenger.

Having established itself on the Atlantic, Virgin is now looking for new routes, and recent moves towards deregulation can have done its prospects no harm. The carrier applied to the British Civil Aviation Authority for permission to operate a service from Gatwick to Maastricht in Holland for an astonishing £15 one way, the cheapest air fare to any European destination. This introductory fare rose to £25 for the Christmas period, and at time of writing load factors on the leased One-Eleven operating on the route averaged a marginal 60%.

The directors feel that the selection of Maastricht, located where the Dutch, Belgian, German borders meet, will not result in direct confrontation with other airlines. At the same time, Maastricht Airport's natural catchment area takes in the populous Ruhr Valley, Southern Holland and Belgium.

But all of this depends on a very high utilisation of Virgin's fleet. Serviceability cannot be guaranteed, and aircraft are subject to comprehensive checks at predetermined intervals. What will happen to the schedules at such times? At present there are other Boeing 747s available for hire — and no doubt their revenue-hungry owners would be only too pleased to oblige — but that situation cannot be counted on to last forever.

In spite of the publicity resources and weighty financial backing that Virgin Atlantic already enjoys, its future will be tolerably secure only when it is able to acquire further routes to other parts of the United States or elsewhere. Europe is obviously important in this respect.

Although the world's only rock-music airline is in fact run on more or less conventional lines, Virgin has brought a touch of show-business panache to the air transport business, and so far that has meant nothing but good news for shareholders and passengers alike.

New look for America's citizen air force

Michael Taylor

Anyone of the opinion that America's Air National Guard (ANG) and US Air Force Reserve (AFRES) are made up of civilian amateurs playing a professional's game could not be further from the truth. The ANG and AFRES use 117 major bases of which only 32 are shared with the fully active USAF. The ANG operates no fewer than 91 air squadrons equipped with 19 types of fixed and rotary-winged aircraft. It has to be ready to act both as a part of the USAF in wartime and as a federal force when called upon to assist in times of national emergency, disaster or civil unrest.

The Guard is of truly staggering significance to total Air Force strength. For example, nearly 70% of the USAF's home fighter-interceptor force comprises ANG units, equipped at present with Convair F-106 Delta Darts and F-4C/D Phantom IIs. It also provides a quarter of the Air Force's tactical fighter force, as well as half the tactical reconnaissance force, equipped with RF-4Cs. There are also major contributions to the USAF's tactical support and airlift, electronic warfare, flight refuelling and rescue capabilities.

AFRES has 56 squadrons, ranging from tactical fighter units, equipped with F-16s, A10As and Phantom IIs, to weather reconnaissance aircraft. In 1983 it played an active role in the multi-nation Grenada intervention, evacuating American citizens, and performed airlift missions on behalf of the US Marines in Lebanon. Less well known but nevertheless important activities that year included airlifting relief supplies to earthquake victims in Colombia and anti-mosquito spraying duties in Minnesota.

Heading picture: **The A-10A is one of the most modern aircraft issued to the ANG. This example is operated by the 104th Tactical Fighter Group, based at Westfield, Massachusetts.** *(Erik Simonsen)*

Above: **The 120th Fighter Interceptor Group, based at Great Falls, Montana, is one of three ANG groups and a wing that fly the F-106 Delta Dart.**

Left: **C-130 Hercules transports of the 133rd Tactical Airlift Wing, based in Minnesota.** *(Erik Simonsen)*

Right: **1st Lt Billy Bell adjusts his parachute harness while his weapon systems operator, 2nd Lt Virgil Wald, scrambles aboard an F-4C Phantom II of the 188th Tactical Fighter Group, based at Fort Smith, Arkansas.** *(US Air Force)*

The value of the ANG/AFRES contribution to the USAF's strength is now being acknowledged through a policy of upgrading these reserve forces and supplying them with some of the latest aircraft types. This year the 159th Tactical Fighter group, based at New Orleans, will discard its F-4Cs to become the first ANG unit to fly F-15 Eagles, while in 1986 another unit will switch from F-4Cs to F-16s. In 1984 the F-16 entered service as an F-105 replacement with one squadron of the AFRES, the 466th TFS in Utah, while this year the C-5A Galaxy is expected to equip part of an airlift wing at Kelly AFB, Texas, following the debut of the C-5B with the full-time Air Force.

But this partial modernisation of the ANG and AFRES cannot hide the fact that the rest of their equipment is beginning to look middle-aged. The active USAF's own aircraft have an average age of nearly 14 years, for alongside the modern F-15s, F-16s and A-10s have to be counted nearly 900 Phantoms approaching 14 years, more than 360 Hercules averaging 16, 273 B-52 Stratofortress strategic bombers at 23, and no fewer than 1,843 other aircraft averaging between 20 and 27 years. The ANG is in worse straits, however, operating slightly more than 1,700 aircraft of

These F-4Cs of the 188th TFG have just arrived at Howard AFB, Panama, for an exercise designed to test the US forces' ability to defend the Canal against attack. The Phantom's travel pods are being removed and replaced with bombs. *(US Air Force)*

all types, of which only some 180 average six years old or less. More than 800 others average between six and 18, leaving nearly 650 still older. Top of the longevity league is the small fleet of C-131s, averaging nearly 29 years. Only slightly younger are the ANG's T-33 trainers. Most significant are the 100 or so KC-135s, averaging over 25 years and equipping four air refuelling

wings and nine groups. Average age of ANG equipment as a whole is about 16 years.

AFRES had 458 aircraft in 1984, of which only 120 averaged less than 15 years old. Almost a quarter of its strength is made up of F-4C and D Phantom IIs averaging over 16 years old and flown by five tactical fighter squadrons. Oldest AFRES type is the AC-130A, at more than 27 years.

In 1983 the USAF, ANG and AFRES together flew more hours than for several years, with the reserve force accumulating nearly a sixth of the total. If this remarkable record is to be bettered, the tempo of re-equipment will have to quicken still more in 1985-86.

Russia's sea-skimming surface raider

Roy McLeavy

Fast surface raiders, designed to make surprise attacks on enemy merchant shipping, have been in use since the beginning of naval history. Early examples were used by the Phoenicians, Greeks and Romans for attacking and plundering commercial craft in enemy coastal waters and ports. In more recent times their successes were emulated by the armed merchantmen operated by the German Naval High Command in the two world wars.

The advantages of disrupting and paralysing enemy sea trade by this method have long been recognised by the Soviet Navy. In any future conflict one of its major aims would be the destruction of enemy sea communications through the use of submarines, surface ships and long-range aircraft. Also destined to take part in these activities is the Soviet Navy's latest and most sophisticated warship-cum-aeroplane, a 560km/hr (350mph) wing-in-ground-effect (WIG) machine mounting two or more SS-N-22 sea-skimming missiles.

The design being developed for this purpose is about 61m (200ft) long, has a span of 30.5m (100ft) and cruises at 280-465km/hr (175-290mph). Main powerp-lant is thought to be a version of the world's most powerful turboprop engine, the Kuznetsov NK-12, driving four-blade contra-rotating propellers. (As the NK-12MA this engine is rated at 11,185kW (15,000shp) and powers the Antonov An-22 military transport, driving propellers 6.20m (20ft 4in) in diameter.) Two smaller gas turbines, mounted forward and exhausting through rotating nozzles, are normally employed only during take-off and landing. Although the vehicle (known to NATO by the code name Casp-B) is intended primarily for operations in the Baltic, North Sea and Mediterranean, it could be deployed from Soviet bases in any part of the world. Fully amphibious, it can skim the sea surface, hover on and off beaches and fly like an aircraft, probably to an altitude of about 3,050m (10,000ft).

The Russian term for WIG is *ekranoplan* (*ekran*, a screen or curtain, and *plan*, the principal lift-generating surface of an aeroplane). An *ekranoplan*

Heading picture: **Impression of Casp-B cruising on its air cushion and, in the background, a sister craft taking off for full flight.**

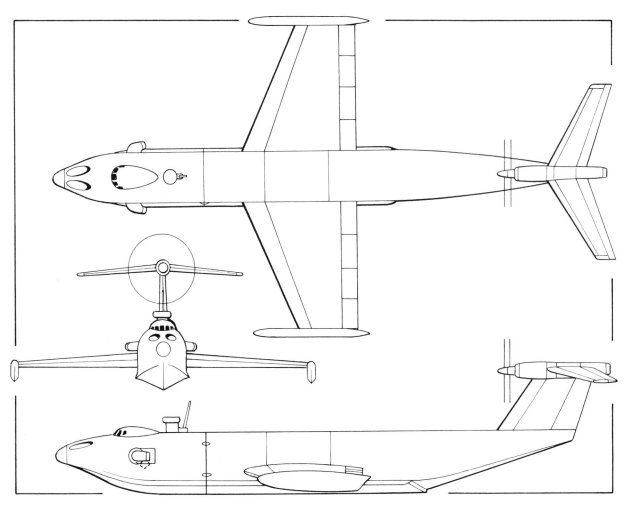

Provisional 3-view of Casp-B showing the rotating nozzles of the two internally mounted PAR jets, their flush air intakes and the Kuznetsov NK-12MV turboprop mounted at the fin/tailplane junction.

Above right: **Radio-controlled model used to demonstrate the PAR-WIG concept.** *(US Navy)*

Right: **Air from the two forward ducted fans of the PAR-WIG model is directed beneath the wing to raise the craft bodily out of the water.**

operates on the principle that, at a height equal to one fifth of its wing span or less, a cushion of air is trapped between the underside of the wings and the land or sea surface below. The closer to the surface the vehicle flies, the more effective the air cushion. Flight within this ground effect inhibits the downwash created by wing lift, reducing induced drag by about 70%. This improves the total lift-to-drag ratio, which in turn reduces fuel consumption and permits the payload or the range to be increased.

Early Soviet test craft like the ESKA-1 showed that whereas an average aircraft at normal flight altitude carries about 4kg (9lb) per hp of engine output, a WIG can carry up to 20kg (44lb), an improvement of 500%. Weight efficiency (ratio of useful load to all-up weight) is 25 to 50%, depending on the size of the craft.

WIGs can fly in and out of ground effect to clear bridges, fog banks, port installations, shipping and shorelines. At altitude they manoeuvre in much the same way as aircraft, but once out of ground effect they

lose their economic advantages, since in order to gain and maintain height they have to operate at increased power.

A vital component of the Soviet Navy's WIG is a system which blows air beneath the mainplane to lift the craft bodily out of the water at 18-27km/hr (11-17mph). This "power-augmented-ram wing-in-ground-effect" (PAR-WIG) arrangement calls for the location of propulsors ahead of the wing to create lift at the low speeds attained during take-off and landing. Hydrodynamic loads at take-off are thus significantly lowered, permitting a reduction in installed thrust, while the use of PAR during landing minimises water impact on the wings and hull, allowing a reduction in structural weight.

The PAR surface on the Soviet missile craft is in the form of a low-aspect-ratio mainplane which is pressurised at low speeds by the efflux of two forward-

Left and above: **Jörg IV Skimcraft, built in West Germany, is one of the few ram wings being developed outside the Soviet Union. It cruises at 80mph and can operate in 1.2m (4ft) waves. Unlike** most of the Soviet concepts, it is not designed to operate as an aircraft. It incorporates features which ensure that it remains within ground effect and thus operates with maximum economy.

located, internally mounted gas turbines. At take-off both the forward and the main powerplants, the latter installed at the top of the T-fin, are used. While manoeuvring at low speed, during take-off and while flying through hump speed (the speed at which wave-making drag is greatest), the forward powerplants are fed by flush intakes in the nose of the upper hull ahead of the control cabin, and exhaust through nozzles below the crew cabin. The exhaust nozzles are rotated downwards to direct their efflux into the volume bounded by the wing undersurface, endplates, extended trailing-edge flaps and the water or other surface below. Within a short distance the craft is lifted out of the water on a cushion of air.

After take-off and during acceleration to cruising speed the nozzles are rotated upwards to align their efflux with the line of flight. Once cruising speed has been reached and the craft is on course, the wing flaps are retracted. The forward gas turbines are shut down, their intakes closed and their nozzles withdrawn into the hull, and the craft then cruises on the power of its contra-rotating turboprop. Sonic/electronic sensor systems match flying height to the prevailing sea conditions.

The missile-carrying *ekranoplan* is a new version of the Casp-B amphibious assault craft, the nose of which is hinged to open aft of the flight deck and forward engine bays to permit the loading of troops, their weapons, equipment and vehicles. With its long range, high speed, heavy lift capacity and shore delivery, it offers many advantages over the ships and aircraft normally used for sea and airlift operations. It can carry assault troops to selected landing zones with little regard for the condition of the sea, tidal currents, underwater obstacles and minefields. Advantages in the battle zone include high-speed manoeuvring and a great reduction in the time taken to undertake individual missions compared with conventional landing craft. Craft of this kind would almost certainly be used to spearhead assault landings at vital defensive positions such as the choke points on the Bosphorous and in the Baltic, Mediterranean and North seas.

For many years the Soviet Navy has sought overseas bases from which to develop its sea power. During the past two decades it has managed to achieve this by supplying naval equipment to regimes which it wishes to befriend. This is the first step in a process that has subsequently led to the acquisition of offshore anchorages and, finally, full basing rights. Significantly, most of the nations approached in this manner are in strategic locations adjacent to choke points, major sea lanes or oil tanker routes. Operating from these bases, as well as from the Soviet Union and Warsaw pact countries, the PAR-WIG *ekranoplan* would prove to be a formidable adversary.

During the Second World War and afterwards until Admiral Sergei Gorshkov took over as commander-in-chief in 1956 the Soviet Navy was virtually a coastal defence force. Nevertheless, MTBs of the Baltic and Black Sea fleets were operated successfully in the sea raider role, and no doubt some of the tactics evolved at that time are retained to this day. The following extracts from an official account of these activities suggest how Soviet Navy PAR-WIGs might be used: "Our crews undertook combat missions at different times of the day and night. They searched for the enemy independently and in small groups along routes used by his shipping. They delivered blows at the enemy ships while at their anchorages in ports and bays and while they were cruising on the open seas . . . Single craft searched widely for targets on the enemy's communication lines. Many of the commanding officers took advantage of the peculiarities of the rocky enemy shore, cleft by skerries and fjords. As a rule, unexpected attacks from the shore brought success . . . Our craft were employed not only for action against enemy sea communications, but also for laying minefields, landing troops and protecting convoys. They also landed sabotage and reconnaissance groups in the enemy's rear".

Unlike many of their Western counterparts, Soviet naval planners appear to appreciate the value of high speed in naval warfare. Since fast warships can project their influence further than slower units in a given time, they invariably enjoy the tactical advantage. The speed of the Soviet Navy's Casp-B would make it difficult to detect, track and target. It would also be less vulnerable to missiles, bombs, naval gunfire, torpedoes and mines. Countering it would be a problem, and the only obvious countermeasure is the introduction of a similar vehicle with superior speed, seaworthiness, range and firepower.

New aircraft of the year

Michael J. H. Taylor

Many new aircraft made their first flights during the 14-month period from June 1, 1983, to August 1, 1984. This feature highlights in chronological order the more important and interesting of these types.

Robin ATL (France)
Two-seat very light monoplane
First flight: June 17, 1983

In 1981 Avions Pierre Robin began work on the ATL (*Avions Très Léger*), a cheap, very light two-seat monoplane for French flying clubs. The 35 kW (47hp) JPX PAL 1300 three-cylinder air-cooled radial two-stroke engine which powered the first prototype on its maiden flight was developed specially for this aircraft. However, to speed certification the prototype was re-engined with a 41.5kW (56hp) Buchoux-converted 1.835cc Volkswagen car engine, the extra weight of which necessitated sweeping the wings forward to maintain an acceptable centre of gravity.

Though initial production ATLs will also have the more powerful engine, the JPX PAL 1300 will later become standard. An initial order for 30 aircraft came from the French National Aeronautical Federation in November 1983. Deliveries were due to begin in late 1984 or early 1985.

Data: ATL with Buchoux engine
Powerplant: As above
Wing span: 10.00m (32ft 9¾in)
Length overall: 6.70m (21ft 11¾in)
Weight empty: 320kg (705lb)
Max T-O weight: 540kg (1,190lb)
Max level speed at S/L: 97kt (180km/hr; 112mph)
Stalling speed, flaps down: 41kt (75km/hr; 47mph)
Max rate of climb at S/L: 175m (570ft)/min
Service ceiling: 4,115m (13,500ft)
Range with max fuel, at economical cruising speed, no reserves: 432nm (800km; 497 miles)

First prototype Robin ATL club and personal light two-seater.

First prototype de Havilland Canada DHC-8 Dash 8. (DHC)

---

de Havilland Canada DHC-8 Dash 8 (Canada)
Twin-turboprop quiet short-range transport
First flight: June 20, 1983

The Dash 8 was designed as a quiet, fuel-efficient short-range transport in the 30-40-passenger category, to fit into the de Havilland Canada range between the Twin Otter and Dash 7. Four initial prototypes were flown, followed in June 1984 by the first with a production interior.

By mid-1984 the company had received orders for and options on 92 Dash 8s, with the first due to enter service with NorOntair in late 1984. Two versions are available: the Commuter standard local-service version and the extended-range Corporate version.

Powerplant: Two 1,432kW (1,800shp) Pratt & Whitney Canada PW120 turborpops
Accommodation: Standard commuter layout for 36 passengers and baggage. Alternative 38/39-passenger, mixed passenger/cargo or corporate layouts, the latter including possible 17 and 24-seat interiors

Wing span: 25.895m (84ft 11½in)
Length overall: 22.25m (73ft 0in)
Operating weight empty: 9,793kg (21,590lb)
Max payload, passengers: 3,549kg (7,824lb)
Max payload, cargo: 4,268kg (9,410lb)
Max T-O weight: 14,968kg (33,000lb)
Max cruising speed at 13,834kg (30,500lb) AUW, at 4,575m (15,000ft), estimated: 270kt (500km/hr; 311mph)
Max rate of climb at S/L, estimated: 631m (2,070ft)/min
Range with full passenger load, estimated: 890nm (1,650km; 1,025 miles)

Airbus A300B4-600 (International)
Wide-bodied medium-range airliner
First flight: July 8, 1983

The A300B4-600 is an advanced version of the B4-200. It incorporates many improvements, including increased passenger and freight capacity. Modifications include the adoption of the rear fuselage

---

Airbus A300-600 in Saudi Arabian Airlines insignia. (GIFAS)

developed for the A310, shorter by two frame pitches in the unpressurised section than that of the A300 Series 100 and 200, with a 0.52m (1ft 9in) extension of the parallel section of the fuselage to re-establish the tail moment arm. Passenger capacity is therefore increased by two rows of seats for an increase in overall length equivalent to only one frame pitch. Other updates include a forward-facing two-man cockpit with CRT displays and new digital avionics, braking control system and APU.

A weight-reduction programme, which called for simplified systems and the use of composite materials for some secondary structural components, allows a greater payload capacity, while a clean-up of the airframe has improved payload/range capability and offers better fuel economy.

Saudi Arabian Airlines was the first operator to order the Series 600, which has since attracted orders from Abu Dhabi, Kuwait Airways and Thai International. The first was delivered to Saudia on March 26, 1984. Aircraft ordered to date are specified with General Electric CF6-80C2-A, Pratt & Whitney JT9D-7R4H1, PW4156 or PW4058 engines. The A300-600 is also available in C and F convertible/freighter versions.

Powerplant: As above
Wing span: 44.84m (147ft 1in)
Length overall: 54.08m (177ft 5in)
Manufacturer's empty weight with JT9D engines: 79,780kg (175,884lb)
Max payload (structural) with JT9D engines: 41,072kg (90,548lb)
Max T-O weight: 165,000kg (363,760lb)
Max cruising speed at 7,620m (25,000ft): 480kt (890km/hr; 553mph)

Max operating altitude: 12,200m (40,000ft)
Range with 267 passengers and baggage, reserves for 200nm (370km; 230 mile) diversion with Pratt & Whitney engines: 3,545nm (6,570km; 4,082 miles)
Range with passengers and reserves as above, with General Electric engines: 3,730nm (6,912km; 4,295 miles)

Embraer EMB-120 Brasilia (Brazil)
Twin-turboprop general-purpose transport
First flight: July 27, 1983

The Brasilia passenger and cargo transport is available with both civil and military interiors. Three prototypes have flown to date and deliveries of production aircraft against orders for and options on 118 aircraft by mid-1984 are expected to begin in mid-1985. Options include 26 military examples for the air forces of Brazil and Chile. Future military versions under development include models for maritime patrol and ECM.

Powerplant: Two 1,185kW (1,590shp) Pratt & Whitney PW115 turboprops
Accommodation: Thirty passengers and attendant in main cabin, or all-cargo interior. Executive or military transport interiors available, plus mixed-traffic version for 24 or 26 passengers and 900kg (1,984lb) of cargo in enlarged rear baggage compartment
Wing span: 19.78m (64ft 10¾in)
Length overall: 20.00m (65ft 7in)
Weight empty, equipped, 30 passengers: 6,459kg (14,240lb)

Second prototype EMB-120 Brasilia. *(Embraer)*

Weight empty, equipped, cargo: 6,168kg (13,598lb)
Max payload, 30 passengers: 3,265kg (7,198lb)
Max payload, cargo: 3,664kg (8,078lb)
Max T-O weight: 10,800kg (23,810lb)
Max level speed at 6,100m (20,000ft): 312kt (578km/hr; 359mph)
Max cruising speed at 6,100m (20,000ft): 294kt (545km/hr; 338mph)
Max rate of climb at S/L: 707m (2,320ft)/min
Service ceiling: 8,990m (29,500ft)
Range at 7,620m (25,000ft), reserves for 100nm (185km; 115 mile) diversion and 45min hold, with 2,721kg (6,000lb) payload: 600nm (1,112km; 691 miles)

Pre-production Vinten-Wallis Venom in Army camouflage. *(Vinten)*

Mitsubishi T-2CCV experimental control-configured vehicle. *(Mitsubishi)*

Vinten Wallis WA-116 Venom (UK)

Single-seat autogyro
First flight: July 29, 1983

Wg Cdr Wallis, well known for his custom-built record-breaking autogyros, and W. Vinten Ltd are to series-produce WA-116s for various civil and military roles. These include air observation, aerial despatch, photography, reconnaissance, fishery survey and protection, cropspraying and other agricultural work, geophysical survey, traffic control, powerline and pipeline inspection, and border patrol. At present there are no plans to sell WA-116s to private individuals. The first of a number of pre-production Venoms flew for the first time in July 1983.

Powerplant: One 59.7-82kW (80-110hp) air-cooled engine. The first pre-production Venom is fitted with a 59.7kW (80hp) Weslake flat-twin
Rotor diameter: 6.15m (20ft 2in)
Length overall, excluding rotor: 3.38m (11ft 1in)
Weight empty: 145kg (320lb)
Max T-O weight: 317kg (700lb)
Max level speed, estimated: 90kt (167km/hr; 103mph)
Cruising speed, estimated: 70kt (130km/hr; 81mph)
Max rate of climb at S/L, estimated: 305m (1,000ft)/min
Service ceiling, estimated: 3,050m (10,000ft)
Still-air range, estimated: 150nm (278km; 173 miles)
Endurance, estimated: 2-3hr

Mitsubishi T-2CCV (Japan)

Control-configured vehicle (CCV) research aircraft
First flight: August 9, 1983

The single-seat T-2CCV is a Mitsubishi T-2 modified for use in the development of active flight control technologies. Modifications include installation of triplex

digital fly-by-wire computers, flight control actuators, manoeuvring flaps, and canards made of carbon-fibre-reinforced plastics. CCV modes to be investigated are control augmentation, relaxed static stability, manoeuvre load control, direct lift control, and direct sideforce control.

The T-2CCV was delivered to the Technical Research and Development Institute of the Japan Defence Agency on March 26, 1984 and over the following two years will be test-flown by the Air Proving Wing of the JASDF.

Powerplant: Two 32.49kN (7,305lb st) with afterburning Rolls-Royce/Turboméca Adour Mk 801A turbofans
Dimensions and performance: As for T-2 except
Horizontal canard span: 4.50m (14ft 9¼in)
Never-exceed speed: Mach 1.4 or 650kt (1,204km/hr; 748mph) EAS

Trago Mills SAH-1 (UK)
Two-seat fully-aerobatic light monoplane
First flight: August 23, 1983

The SAH-1 is a side-by-side two-seat trainer with baggage space to the rear of the seats. It is made of aluminium alloy stabilised with PVC foam. The basic version is powered by an 88kW (118hp) Avco Lycoming O-235-L2A flat-four engine, but a more powerful model with a 119kW (160hp) AEIO-320-DB is expected to be available at a later date.

Trago Mills SAH-1 two-seat aerobatic aircraft.

Data: 118hp version
Powerplant: As above
Wing span: 9.36m (30ft 8½in)
Length overall: 6.58m (21ft 7¼in)
Weight empty: 460kg (1,014lb)
Max T-O weight: 748kg (1,649lb)
Max level speed: 121kt (224km/hr; 139mph)
Stalling speed, flaps down: 47kt (88 km/hr; 55mph) EAS
Max rate of climb at S/L: 279m (915ft)/min
Service ceiling: 5,000m (16,400ft)
Range with max fuel, 13.6lit (3 Imp gal) reserves, at 78kt (145km/hr; 90mph) at 1,525m (5,000ft): 620nm (1,149km; 714 miles)

Skyfox Trainer (USA)
Tandem two-seat jet trainer
First flight: August 23, 1983

Skyfox Corporation has designed and developed a derivative of the Lockheed T-33 jet trainer, between 1,000 and 1,500 of which are believed still to be in existence. Retaining some 70% of the original basic structure, the conversion from T-33 to Skyfox transforms the aircraft into an advanced tactical combat trainer powered by two modern engines in place of the T-33's single unit. Modern avionics and equipment are fitted, and the airframe itself is refurbished and updated. The resulting aircraft is significantly cheaper than but comparable in performance with newly built advanced jet trainers.

Apart from the engine modifications, a swept vertical tail with mid-mounted tailplane is fitted, the wingtips

Prototype Skyfox trainer standing in front of a standard T-33.

carry downward-canted winglets and the forward fuselage has new contours. Stencel ejection seats are installed and tip tanks may be carried to extend range. Subject to finalisation of an agreement, the first 20 Skyfoxes will go to the Portuguese Air Force.

Powerplant: Two 16.46kN (3,700lb st) Garrett TFE731-3 turbofans mounted in pods on either side of the rear fuselage
Wing span: 11.84m (38ft 10in)
Length overall: 14.02m (46ft 0in)
Weight empty: 3,856kg (8,500lb)
Max T-O weight: 6,532kg (14,400lb) clean
Max level speed at S/L: 505kt (935km/hr; 581mph)
Max rate of climb at S/L: 3,050m (10,000ft)
Range, internal fuel only: 2,250nm (4,169km; 2,591 miles)
g limit: +7.33

Beechcraft Model 2000 Starship 1 scale prototype (USA)
85%-scale proof-of-concept aircraft
First flight: August 29, 1983

Built by Burt Rutan's Scaled Composites Inc, the 85%-scale prototype of the projected Beechcraft Model 2000 Starship 1 was built to provide data for the full-size aircraft, six pre-production examples of which are to be completed initially. The first full-size pre-production aircraft is expected to fly for the first time towards the end of 1985.

The Starship 1 will be an eight/eleven-seat business aircraft of composite construction with rear-mounted sweptback wings carrying wingtip stabilisers and the two 746kW (1,000hp) Pratt & Whitney Canada PT6A-60A turboprops driving pusher propellers. Variable-geometry sweptback foreplanes are mounted low on the nose, and the tricycle landing gear is retractable.

Data: Full-size Starship 1
Powerplant: As above
Wing span: 16.62m (54ft 6½in)
Foreplane span, zero sweep: 7.54m (24ft 9in)
Length overall: 14.05m (46ft 1in)
Weight empty, standard, equipped: 3,489kg (7,693lb)
Max payload: 1,409kg (3,107lb)
Max T-O weight: 5,670kg (12,500lb)
Max level speed and max cruising speed at 7,620m (25,000ft), estimated: 365kt (676km/hr; 420mph)
Max rate of climb at S/L, estimated: 1,000m (3,280ft)/min

The Scale Composites 85%-scale prototype of the Beechcraft Model 2000 Starship 1.

Service ceiling, estimated: 12,130m (39,800ft)
Range with max fuel, long-range cruise power, 45min reserves, estimated: 2,687nm (4,979km; 3,094 miles)

Hunting Firecracker (UK)
Two-seat trainer
First flight (NDN 1T Turbo Firecracker): September 1, 1983

Hunting Firecracker Aircraft Ltd was founded in September 1984 to bid for the contract to replace the RAF's Jet Provosts. The Firecracker trainer itself had been designed and certificated by NDN Aircraft and manufactured by Firecracker Aircraft.

The prototype of the turbine-engined Firecracker flew for the first time in September 1983 and was certificated in March of the following year. It is one of two aircraft acquired subsequently by Specialist Flying Training Ltd. A third Firecracker was being built in 1984. Both civil and military Firecrackers are offered, the latter having the more powerful 559kW (750shp) Pratt & Whitney PT6A-25D.

Data: Civil Firecracker, unless otherwise stated
Powerplant: One 533kW (715eshp) Pratt & Whitney PT6A-25A turboprop
Wing span: 7.92m (26ft 0in)
Length overall: 8.33m (27ft 4in)
Weight empty, equipped: 1,066kg (2,350lb)
Weight empty, equipped, military version: 1,210kg (2,667lb)
Max T-O weight: 1,633kg (3,600lb)
Max T-O weight, military version: 1,832kg (4,040lb)
Military overload T-O weight: 1,927kg (4,250lb)

Max level speed at 4,575m (15,000ft): 198kt (367km/hr; 228mph)
Stalling speed, flaps down and engine idling: 60kt (111km/hr; 69mph) EAS
Max rate of climb at S/L: 628m (2,060ft)/min
Service ceiling: 8,260m (27,100ft)
Range with max standard fuel, no reserves: 625nm (1,158km; 720 miles)
g limits at normal T-O weight: +6/−3
Armament: Four underwing hardpoints on military version, each of 181kg (400lb) capacity, for auxiliary fuel tanks, gun pods, rocket launchers, bombs, photo-reconnaissance pods, etc

One of two Firecrackers acquired by Specialist Flying Training Ltd.

First prototype Agusta A129 Mangusta armed attack helicopter. *(Agusta)*

Agusta A 129 Mangusta (Italy)
Light anti-tank, attack and scout helicopter
First flight: September 15, 1983

The A 129 will serve with the Italian Army as a specialised attack helicopter, carrying anti-tank or area-suppression weapons, and will have full night/bad weather combat capability. It can also perform the advanced scouting role. Two Italian Army squadrons totalling 60 aircraft will deploy it initially, with a further six aircraft being used for training purposes. The first are due to enter service in 1986. A further 30 aircraft, plus reserves, may follow.

Export Mangustas would have General Electric T700-GE-701 or -401 engines and, possibly, alternative avionics and equipment.

The fuselage, which accommodates the pilot and co-pilot/gunner in stepped, separate tandem cockpits, is a conventional semi-monocoque structure of aluminium alloy longerons and frames, with honeycomb panels in the centre fuselage and fuel tank areas. Composite materials are used for the nosecone, tailboom, tail rotor pylon, engine nacelles, canopy frame and maintenance panels. The airframe has an infrared-absorbing paint finish and can tolerate 12.7mm armour-piercing ammunition.

Powerplant: Two 607.5kW (815shp) Rolls-Royce Gem 2 Mk 1004D turboshafts
Main rotor diameter: 11.90m (39ft 0½in)
Wing span: 3.20m (10ft 6in)
Length of fuselage: 12.275m (40ft 3¼in)
Weight empty, equipped: 2,529kg (5,575lb)
Max external weapons load: 1,000kg (2,205lb)
Max design T-O weight: 3,700kg (8,157lb)
Max level speed at S/L, estimated: 145kt (270km/hr; 168mph)
Max rate of climb at S/L, estimated: 637m (2,090ft)/min
Hovering ceiling, in ground effect, estimated: 3,290m (10,800ft)
Max endurance, no reserves, estimated: 3hr
g limits: +3.5/−0

Reims-Cessna 406-5 Caravan II (France/USA)
Twin-turboprop business and utility monoplane
First flight: September 22, 1983

This variant of Cessna's 400 series of light twin transports is being manufactured and marketed by Reims in France, using wings supplied by Cessna. A crew of two and ten or twelve passengers can be accommodated; a VIP executive version has six passenger seats.

Powerplant: Two 373kW (500shp) Pratt & Whitney PT6A-112 turboprops
Wing span: 15.04m (49ft 4¼in)
Length overall: 11.89m (39ft 0in)
Weight empty: 2,250kg (4,961lb)
Max payload: 1,534kg (3,382lb)
Max T-O weight: 4,246kg (9,360lb)
Max cruising speed at 4,575m (15,000ft) at AUW of 3,628kg (8,000lb), estimated: 256kt (474km/hr; 294mph)

Prototype Reims-Cessna 406-5 Caravan II. *(GIFAS)*

Max rate of climb at S/L, estimated: 560m (1,835ft)/min
Service ceiling: 9,450m (31,000ft)
Range with max fuel, at 247kt (457km/hr; 284mph) at 3,050m (10,000ft), estimated: 1,000nm (1,852km; 1,150 miles)
Range with max payload at max cruising speed, 45min reserves, estimated: 120nm (222km; 138 miles)

Airtech (CASA/Nurtanio) CN-235 (Spain/Indonesia)
Twin-turboprop commuter and utility airliner
First flight: November 11, 1983

The CN-235 commuter and utility airliner was optimised for short-haul operations, with the result that it can fly four 100nm (185km; 115-mile) stage lengths with reserves before having to refuel. It can operate from either paved runways or unprepared strips.

A joint development and production effort by CASA of Spain and Nurtanio of Indonesia, the CN-235 is marketed by the Spanish company in America and Europe and by Nurtanio in Asia, with other markets shared. By March 1984 a total of 110 CN-235s had been ordered by airlines and air forces, with options on 23 more. The intention is to produce three aircraft per month in each country. The first prototype to fly was completed in Spain, with Nurtanio's following it into the air on December 30, 1983.

Powerplant: Two 1,268kW (1,700shp) General Electric CT7-7 turboprops
Wing span: 25.81m (84ft 8in)
Length overall: 21.353m (70ft 0¾in)
Operating weight empty: 9,400kg (20,725lb)
Max payload, passengers: 4,200kg (9,260lb)
Max payload, cargo: 5,000kg (11,025lb)
Max payload, military version: 4,135kg (9,116lb)

Indonesian-assembled prototype Airtech CN-235 transport. *(Nurtanio)*

Max T-O weight: 14,400kg (31,745lb)
Max cruising speed at 4,575m (15,000ft): 244kt (452km/hr; 280mph)
Service ceiling: 7,925m (26,000ft)
Range with reserves for 100nm (185km; 115-mile) diversion and 45min hold, with 44 passengers: 418nm (775km; 481 miles)
Range of military version, estimated, with 45min reserves, max payload, max cruising speed at 5,485m (18,000ft): 518nm (960km; 596 miles)
Range of military version, estimated with 45min reserves, with 1,000kg (2,205lb) payload, long-range cruising speed at 6,100m (20,000ft): 2,398nm (4,445km; 2,762 miles)

Bell AH-1T+ SuperCobra (USA)

Close support and attack helicopter
First flight: November 16, 1983

During 1980 Bell fitted two General Electric T700-GE-700 turboshafts (combined output of over 2,386kW; 3,200shp) to a USMC AH-1T as part of its attack helicopter research and development effort. Improvements proposed for retrofit to existing AH-1Ts included installation of General Electric T700-GE-401 turboshafts (combined output of 2,423kW; 3,250shp), a new combining gearbox, and a number of detail changes. The T700-GE-401-powered AH-1T+ was evaluated by the USMC from December 1983. Early in 1984 Congress approved the purchase of 44 AH-1T+ SuperCobras, with deliveries to begin in 1986. Missions include anti-armour, troop-carrying helicopter escort, multiple-weapon fire support, reconnaissance, and search and target acquisition.

Powerplant: As above
Armament: 76 2.75in or 16 5in Zuni rockets, or two AIM-9L Sidewinder or Stinger air-to-air missiles plus 750 rounds of 20mm ammunition, or up to eight TOW or Hellfire anti-tank missiles
Max cruising speed: 160kt (296km/hr; 184mph)

Zlin Z-37T (Czechoslovakia)

Single-seat agricultural aircraft
First flight: July 12, 1983

This is a lower-powered turbine-engined version of the XZ-37T prototype of 1981, which was itself based on the piston-engined Z-37A Cmeläk. It has a maximum hopper/tank capacity of 1,000lit (220 Imp gal) of liquid or 800kg (1,764lb) of dry chemical.

Powerplant: One 365kW (490shp) Motorlet M601Z turboprop
Wing span: 12.95m (42ft 6in)
Length overall (flying attitude): 10.46m (34ft 4in)
Weight empty with basic agricultural equipment: 1,350kg (2,976lb)
Max payload: 800kg (1,764lb)
Max T-O weight: 2,400kg (5,291lb)
Max level speed at 500m (1,640ft): 124kt (230km/hr; 143mph)
Stalling speed, flaps down: 47kt (87km/hr; 54mph)
Range with max fuel: 162nm (300km; 186 miles)

Prototype Zlin Z-37T agricultural aircraft.

Prototype Sikorsky HH-60A Night Hawk combat rescue helicopter.

Sikorsky HH-60A Night Hawk (USA)
Combat rescue helicopter
First flight: February 4, 1984

The HH-60A version of the Sikorsky S-70 for the USAF is designed to perform unescorted day/night combat rescue missions at treetop level over a radius of 250nm (463km; 287 miles) without refuelling. This variant replaced the HH-60D all-weather version and reduced-capability HH-60E, which were cancelled in 1984.

The prototype HH-60A is equipped with a rescue hoist, internal and external auxiliary fuel tanks, an air-air refuelling probe, additional avionics and cabin fittings for the installation of rescue equipment. Production HH-60As will be powered by uprated (1,260kW; 1,690shp) T700-GE-401s, while the transmission, rotor brake, approach/hover coupler and rescue hoist will be similar to those fitted to the Seahawk.

Pilot and co-pilot will have night vision goggles. Defensive equipment will include a radar warning receiver, flare/chaff dispenser, and provision for an infra-red jammer and 7.62mm machine guns. There will be accommodation for two crew and ten passengers. The USAF intends to acquire 90 Night Hawks, with deliveries starting in 1988.

Powerplant: As above
Main rotor diameter: 16.36m (53ft 8in)
Length of fuselage, including retracted refuelling probe: 17.38m (57ft 0¼in)
Weight empty: 5,734kg (12,642lb)
Mission T-O weight: 9,259kg (20,413lb)
Max level speed at S/L: 145kt (268km/hr; 167mph)
Vertical rate of climb at S/L: 203m (665ft)/min
Endurance: 4hr 51min with max fuel

Boeing 737-300 (USA)
Short-range airliner
First flight: February 24, 1984

The airframe of the 737-300 is about 70% common with that of the Advanced 737-200. Lengthening of the fuselage, to accommodate additional passengers and underfloor freight, and the installation of new-generation turbofans offer much reduced fuel consumption per seat-mile and lower noise levels compared with the earlier model.

The No 2 Boeing 737-300. Replacement of the 737's original engines with high-bypass ratio CFM56-3s has resulted in reduced noise and fuel consumption. *(Boeing)*

Boeing regards the 737-300 as an addition to its range rather than as a replacement for the 737-200. Orders totalled 129 by mid-September 1984, with deliveries scheduled to begin in November.

Powerplant: Two 89kN (20,000lb st) CFM International CFM56-3 turbofans
Accommodation: Various cabin layouts for between 110 and 149 passengers
Wing span: 28.91m (94ft 10in)
Length overall: 33.40m (109ft 7in)
Operating weight empty: 31,298kg (69,000lb)
Max T-O weight, standard: 56,472kg (124,500lb)
Max T-O weight, optional: 61,235kg (135,000lb)
Still-air range with 140 passengers, estimated at standard T-O weight, T-O at S/L: 1,672nm (3,098km; 1,925 miles)
Still-air range, conditions as above but at optional T-O weight: 2,353nm (4,361km; 2,710 miles)

IAI 1125 Astra (Israel)
Twin-turbofan business aircraft
First flight: March 19, 1984

Known originally as the 1125 Westwind, the Astra is a more comfortable, fuel-efficient and environmentally acceptable development of the Westwind series of business aircraft. The major difference is in the wings, which are swept back and have a new high-efficiency Sigma 2 aerofoil section of IAI design. They are also mounted low on the fuselage so as to pass beneath the cabin floor and thus take up no cabin space. The new wings allow more efficient high-subsonic cruising flight over long ranges, resulting in reduced operating costs.

First prototype IAI Astra business aircraft. *(IAI)*

The Astra's structure contains a higher proportion of composite materials than that of the Westwind. By 1984 ten Astras had been ordered by IAI's North American distributor.

Powerplant: Two 16.23kN (3,650lb st) Garrett TFE731-3B100G turbofans
Accommodation: Crew of two and six to nine passengers
Wing span: 16.05m (52ft 8in)
Length overall: 16.94m (55ft 7in)
Basic operating weight empty: 5,747kg (12,670lb)
Max payload: 1,510kg (3,330lb)
Max T-O weight: 10,659kg (23,500lb)
Max cruising speed, estimated, at 10,670m (35,000ft): 473kt (876km/hr; 545mph)
Max rate of climb at S/L, estimated: 1,085m (3,560 ft)/min
Max certification altitude, estimated: 13,715m (45,000ft)
Range with max fuel, estimated, 5 passengers, with reserves: 2,665-3,337nm (4,939-6,184km; 3,069-3,842 miles)

Pilatus PC-9 (Switzerland)
Single/two-seat trainer
First flight: May 7, 1984

The PC-9 is an advanced, high-performance turboprop trainer suitable for use across the whole flight tuition curriculum. It has only about 10% structural commonality with the PC-7, with differences including the more powerful 857kW (1,150shp) Pratt & Whitney Canada PT6A-62 turboprop, stepped tandem cockpits with ejection seats, a ventral airbrake, modified wing profiles and tips, new ailerons, a longer dorsal fin, mainwheel doors, and larger wheels with high-pressure tyres.

The PC-9 is one of the trainers under consideration by the British Ministry of Defence as a possible RAF

Jet Provost replacement. If the Swiss type is selected, PC-9s for the RAF will be co-produced by BAe.

Powerplant: As above
Wing span: 10.12m (33ft 2½in)
Length overall: 10.05m (32ft 11¾in)
Basic weight empty: approx 1,620kg (3,571lb)
Max T-O weight with underwing loads: 3,200kg (7,055lb)
Max level speed, aerobatic: 300 kt (556km/hr; 345mph)
Stalling speed, engine idling, aerobatic with flaps and landing gear up: 79kt (147km/hr; 91mph) EAS
Max rate of climb at S/L, aerobatic: 1,220m (4,000ft)/min
Service ceiling: 11,580m (38,000ft)
Max range at cruise power at 5,000m (16,400ft), 5% plus 20min reserves: 830nm (1,538km; 955 miles)
Armament: Three hardpoints under each wing; up to 250kg (551lb) of stores on the inboard and central locations and 110kg (242lb) on each outboard. Maximum external stores load 1,040kg (2,293lb)

The two pre-production Pilatus PC-9s.

Lockheed P-3 (AEW&C) Orion (USA)
Airborne early-warning and control aircraft
First flight: June 14, 1984

The P-3 (AEW&C) is a variant of the Orion designed for airborne early-warning and control duties. The prototype is a converted ex-Royal Australian Air Force P-3B with a 7.32m (24ft) diameter APA-171 rotodome mounted above the rear fuselage. The General Electric AN/APS-138 radar, as fitted to the Grumman E-2C Hawkeye, will be installed in 1985 after aerodynamic, performance and loading trials have been completed. Possible purchasers include Australia, Canada, Japan and the US Navy. A similar AEW&C package is being proposed for the C-130 Hercules.

Endurance: approx 14hr

Aerodynamic prototype of the Lockheed P-3 (AEW&C).
(Lockheed)

Westland Lynx 3 (UK)
Twin-engined anti-armour helicopter
First flight: June 14, 1984

The Lynx 3 dedicated anti-tank helicopter is derived from the earlier production Lynx and incorporates its dynamic systems. With a gross weight some 27% greater than that of the earlier Lynx, it offers increased survivability and greater firepower. Advanced avionics, including night vision and target acquisition systems in optional nose, roof and rotor mast mounts, will allow it to operate by day or night and in bad weather. It can be equipped to carry current and future versions of the Hot, TOW and Hellfire anti-tank missiles, and for defence against air attack it can be armed with General Dynamics Stinger missiles. A naval version has also been announced.

Powerplant: Two 832kW (1,115shp) Rolls-Royce Gem 60 turboshafts
Main rotor diameter: 12.80m (42ft 0in)
Length overall, rotors turning: 15.47m (50ft 9in)
Payload: 1,542kg (3,400lb)
Normal max T-O weight: 5,896kg (13,000lb)
Max level speed, estimated: 165kt (306km/hr; 190mph)
Range with max fuel, 20 min reserves, estimated: 335nm (620km; 385 miles)
Endurance: 3hr 30min

Pre-production Westland Lynx 3 with Hellfire missiles and large-calibre guns. *(Westland)*

Bell Model 400 TwinRanger (USA)
Seven-seat twin-engined helicopter
First flight: July 4, 1984

The Model 400 TwinRanger is the first of a new family of commercial and military helicopters which will be designed, developed and manufactured at Bell Helicopter Textron's new Canadian Division in Quebec. This plant is the first helicopter factory in Canada, which is the second largest user of helicopters outside the Soviet bloc. Subsequent members of the TwinRanger family are the Model 400A and Model 440, due to appear in 1987 and 1988 respectively.

Features of the Model 400 include a four-blade "soft-in-plane" main rotor with composite blades and hub, a Ring-Guard tail rotor, an advanced-technology transmission and drive system with run-dry capability, and twin Allison 250-C-20P turboshafts.

Data: Model 400 TwinRanger
Powerplant: As above
Weight empty: 1,410kg (3,110lb)
Max T-O weight: 2,495kg (5,500lb)
Cruising speed, estimated: 140kt (259km/hr; 161mph)
Max range, estimated: 380nm (704km/hr; 437 miles)

Bell Model 400 aerodynamic test prototype. *(Bell)*

BAe Super 748 (UK)
Twin-turboprop transport
First flight: July 30, 1984

The Super 748 is the latest of the 748 series, embodying all the improvements of the earlier Series 2B together with such new developments as an advanced flight deck, new-style galley, and engine hushkits. The 1,700kW (2,280ehp) Dart RDa.7 Mk 552-2 engines offer as much as a 12% reduction in fuel consumption over earlier marks. A system for dynamic balancing of the propellers to reduce cabin vibration and noise levels is optional. Baggage capacity is increased.

Powerplant: As above
Wing span: 31.23m (102ft 5½in)
Length overall: 20.42m (67ft 0in)
Basic operating weight, including crew: 12,327kg (27,176lb)
Max payload: 5,136kg (11,323lb)
Max T-O weight: 21,092kg (46,500lb)
Cruising speed at AUW of 17,236kg (38,000lb): 244 kt (452km/hr; 281mph)
Max rate of climb at S/L, AUW as above: 433m (1,420ft)/min
Service ceiling: 7,620m (25,000ft)
Range with max payload, reserves for 200nm (370km; 230 miles) plus 45min hold: 926nm (1,715km; 1,066 miles)

Fighters return to North Weald

N. B. Rivett

The Battle of Britain airfield at North Weald, Essex, resounded once more to the song of the Merlin for two days last year. The occasion was the debut of a large new display on the air show circuit. The first Fighter Meet was held at the former RAF station, located in London's north-eastern suburbs, during the weekend of June 30 and July 1. The guiding light was Ray Hanna of Red Arrows and Spitfire Mk 9 fame, and the Meet witnessed what was probably the largest gathering of vintage types in recent years. Aircraft put through their flying paces ranged from S.E.5A and Fokker Triplane replicas to a (non-vintage) Sepecat Jaguar.

Combat set-pieces featured mock bombs and examples of the Nord 1002, Pilatus P-2 and Casa 352 (Ju 52) carrying Luftwaffe colours and smoke-making equipment. Motorists on the adjacent M11 motorway must have been surprised to see "German" aircraft trailing smoke across the countryside!

The Meet gave many people their first glimpse of the Curtiss Tomahawk in action and of one of the latest Spitfire restorations, a Mk 9 (G-BJSG/ML417) owned

Repainted in Luftwaffe markings, this Spanish-built CASA 352 has a Curtiss Tomahawk as its unlikely flying partner.

by Stephen Gray.

Whatever they may say, fighter pilots are made, not born, and the trainers used for the job were present in quantity. The Harvard formation was impressive, not least for the engine noise on take-off, and the piston Provost and ex-Red Arrows Gnat were also well displayed.

RAF participation included the Battle of Britain Flight, Vintage Pair, Red Arrows and the Jaguar.

The flying was spirited, to say the least, and many people considered the Meet to have been the best display of Second World War fighters for many years. Asked afterwards if the display would be repeated, Ray Hanna answered: "If it is a success." As far as the big and enthusiastic crowd was concerned the Meet was a huge success, and the first of many more chances to see some classic warbirds in action.

Top: **The CASA 352 wheels smoothly onto the North Weald runway.**

Above: **Stephen Gray's Spitfire Mk 9.**

Below: **Two Spitfire Mk 9s grace the sky over North Weald.**

Left: **Interwar flying was represented by this fine replica of the Fairey Flycatcher carrier fighter.**

Below: **One of the most popular First World War replicas is the Fokker Dr. I triplane, complete with mock Spandau guns.**

Right: **Hawker Sea Fury T.20, one of an original batch of 42 FB.11s and T.20s.**

Below right: **Two of the "Luftwaffe" aircraft in the display: a Swiss Pilatus P-2 and (bottom) a French Nord 1002.**

Here comes the Navy: heading four naval fighters of 1940s vintage is a Grumman F8F Bearcat, followed in quick succession by a Chance Vought F4U-7 Corsair, Grumman F4F Wildcat and Hawker Sea Fury T.20.

Below: F-8F Bearcat follows a P-51D Mustang into the air.

Formation of Harvards, among the most collectable of US vintage aircraft.

Below: **Harvard in South African markings.**

This de Havilland Mosquito T.3 was one of a batch of 50 built at Leavesden.

Above: **No display of vintage warplanes would be complete without at least one Boeing B-17 Flying Fortress.** *Sally B* **is painted in corrosion-resistant drab.**

Top right: **Hawker Hunter T.3 operated by the Institute of Aviation Medicine, Farnborough.**

Red Arrows past and present: an ex-red Arrows Gnat trainer above right **was flown at the Meet and still looked spritely alongside the team's newer BAe Hawks** right.

Right up to date with a Sepecat Jaguar, seen here completing its landing roll with Irvin brake parachute deployed from the fuselage tailcone.

LHX: the fighter pilot's helicopter

Elfan ap Rees

The year is 2000, the scene a battlefield anywhere in the world. Lieutenant Intrepid of the UN Army Air Corps has just landed from his third mission of the day. So far the score is five tanks, several personnel carriers and one enemy attack helicopter, while on this last mission he found and identified a large troop concentration in a forest about 20km away. And it isn't even dawn yet.

Intrepid walks from his helicopter to the briefing tent, taking with him a small tape casette which he has removed from the aircraft's on-board computer. Inside

Heading picture: **Impression of a single-seat LHX incorporating an automated cockpit, voice-actuated controls and "self-healing" avionics.** *(Boeing Vertol)*

103

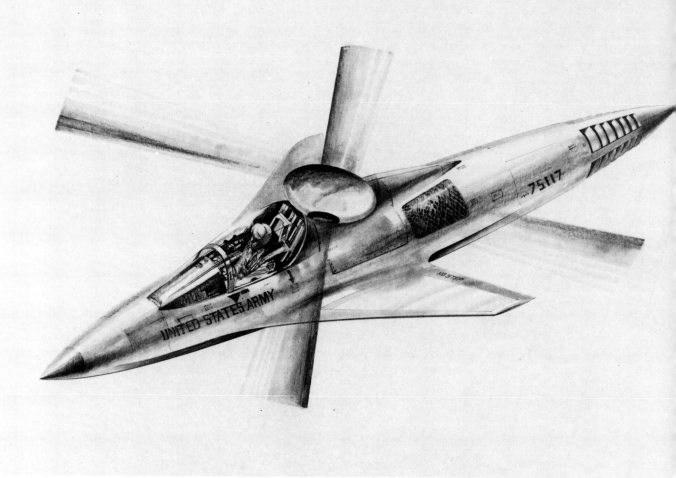

Artist's impression of an LHX SCAT helicopter incorporating NOTAR technology. *(Hughes Helicopters)*

the tent it is inserted into a master computer and, within seconds, the field commander's battle plan is updated with the latest troop positions and a myriad of other details. In addition the squadron maintenance team receive the latest information on Intrepid's aircraft — engine hours, g forces recorded during the mission, malfunctions — and carry out an instant serviceability check.

Unfortunately for the Lieutenant his helicopter is A1, and within a few minutes has been refuelled and rearmed for Mission 4. Soon Intrepid emerges from the briefing tent with a new tape in his hand. On it are details of potential targets, autopilot navigation data, likely threats, armament carried, and other information that may prove useful. The tape is Intrepid's only companion, for this new generation of battlefield helicopter pilot flies alone.

In the mid-1980s it is in fact easier to describe the mission in the year 2000 than the helicopter that will perform it, for the new technology on the horizon offers a variety of configurations for the new generation of

light utility/scout/attack helicopters. In the United States this is LHX, a single helicopter designed to replace the nine diverse types now serving with the US Army in these roles and to back up the heavyweight Hughes AH-64A Apache attack helicopter and the Sikorsky UH-60 Black Hawk and Boeing Vertol CH-47D Chinook troop transports.

LHX is currently the US Army's top aviation priority, with an order for 5,000 aircraft due to go to the winner of the design competition that is now about to begin. Sales to other operators could bring total production to treble or even quadruple this figure. Small wonder then that the four main US helicopter manufacturers, not to mention IBM and the major powerplant companies, are pulling out all the stops in an effort to land the contract.

The US Army specification for LHX is demanding, as is the timescale. The request for proposals will be issued this summer, full-scale development of the selected design is expected to start in early 1987, and service entry is scheduled for the mid-1990s.

Two versions are planned. The first, LHX SCAT (Scout/Attack), will replace the Bell AH-1S, Bell OH-58 and Hughes OH-6 in the air-to-air/air-to-ground defence, reconnaissance and surveillance roles. The second version, intended to replace the Bell UH-1, will be the LHX Utility, a six-passenger transport. Both versions could feature single-pilot cockpits, and will be powered by twin engines offering about 1,000shp apiece.

Armament, sensors and avionics will depend to some extent on the variant, but will certainly be integrated. Weapons are likely to include anti-tank and air-to-air missiles such as Hellfire and Stinger, backed up by a fast-firing cannon and assorted pylon-mounted ordnance. These will be combined with day/night sighting systems and avionics incorporating visual display units, the main aim being to reduce pilot workload while supplying him with the maximum amount of data.

The LHX airframe and dynamics are a long way from being finalised. Stealth technology will certainly be used to minimise the chances of radar and infra-red detection, and the largely composite fuselage will be assembled from preformed sections, rather like a giant plastic construction kit. But beyond that nothing can be settled until the US Army makes its mind up about maximum speed — anywhere between 160 and 300kt — and all-up weight, which could be as little as 2,300kg (5,000lb) or as much as 4,000kg (9,000lb).

Mock-up of Bell's Advanced Tilt Rotor. *(Bell)*

Bell Helicopter is promoting the tilt-rotor, although the company has more conventional plans up its sleeve if the customer decides to keep the maximum speed below 180kt. Bell claims that above this speed the tilt-rotor is the best way to meet the prime mission requirements, offering the fullest combination of high and low-speed performance and nap-of-the-earth manoeuvrability, and overall dimensions no greater than those of the AH-1.

As well as conventional designs, Sikorsky is also offering its Advancing Blade Concept (ABC), with a ducted pusher fan added to the basic ABC layout already tested on the XH-59A. This would take maximum speed up to 250kt.

Hughes and Boeing Vertol have so far stuck with more conventional rotor systems, with and without tail rotors, while IBM teamed up with Aérospatiale to enter the Advanced Rotorcraft Technology Integration (ARTI) programme, one of several current investigations of potential LHX concepts. ARTI is intended primarily to show whether a single pilot can handle the LHX mission. Other comparable efforts include the Advanced Technology Demonstrator Engine (ATDE), being worked on by Allison, Avco-Lycoming, Garrett and Pratt & Whitney, Advanced Digital Optical Control System (ADOCS), Integrated Technology Rotor (ITR), NOTAR (No Tail Rotor), and Advanced Composite Airframe Programme (ACAP).

Sikorsky XH-59A Advancing Blade Concept (ABC) research helicopter.

Several of these programmes have already resulted in flying hardware, particularly ACAP, for which Bell and Sikorsky have produced prototypes combining composite airframes with conventional dynamics. It could therefore be argued that LHX is in fact already off the ground and spearheading a major revolution in light helicopter manufacturing and technology. Meanwhile, Lieutenant Intrepid has probably just celebrated his tenth birthday and is already well versed in the computerised war games that he might one day play for real.

Shorts: thriving on co-operation

Tim Wrixon

1984 saw the 75th anniversary of the flight of the first aircraft to be designed and built by the Short Brothers. Now the most significant UK manufacturer of fixed-wing aircraft outside British Aerospace, the company enters its fourth quarter-century with a sound product range of its own, plus a profitable array of subcontracting and collaborative ventures. The latest of these was on spectacular view at last September's Farnborough Show, where two Embraer Tucano turboprop-powered trainers put on one of the most breathtaking displays of the week.

Belfast-based Shorts teamed up with Brazil's Embraer to promote the elegant Tucano as a contender in the RAF's Jet Provost replacement competition. Also in with a chance of becoming the RAF's new basic trainer were the Swiss Pilatus PC-9, the subject of a co-operative agreement with British Aerospace; the Australian Aircraft Consortium A20 Wamira, in which Westland has an interest; and the British-designed

Firecracker, to be built by Hunting Firecracker Aircraft. Even at this stage the RAF may yet decide to meet the requirement by refurbishing the Jet Provost fleet. But if it opts for a new type the Shorts Tucano stands a very good chance of selection — and that would mean an order for 130 aircraft. It is already in service with the Brazilian Air Force and is said to need little modification to bring it up to the RAF specification.

Shorts' other collaborative efforts are already contributing to the company's prosperity. Apart from the design, development and production of its own Skyvan, 330 and 360 light transports, Shorts makes major aircraft components for other companies in Europe and

---

Heading picture: **The Brazilian-designed Tucano turboprop trainer, being offered by Shorts as a replacement for the RAF's Jet Provosts.** *(Shorts)*

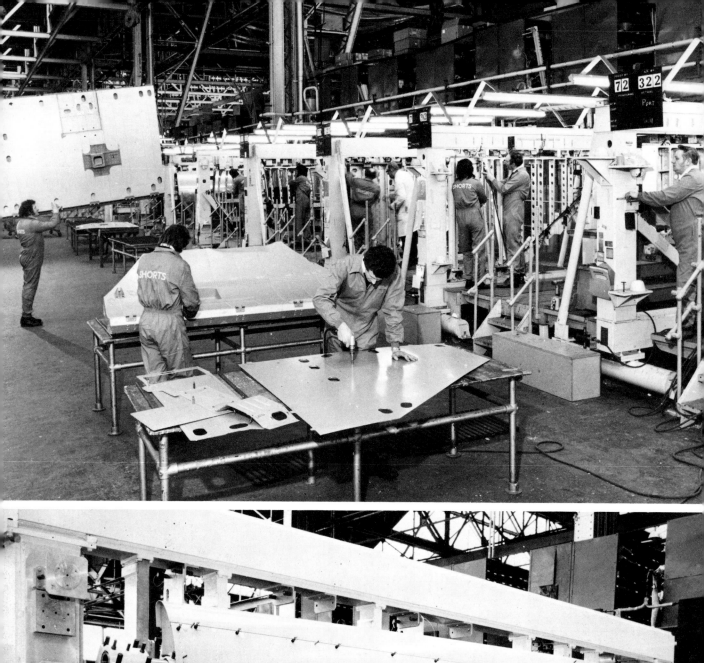

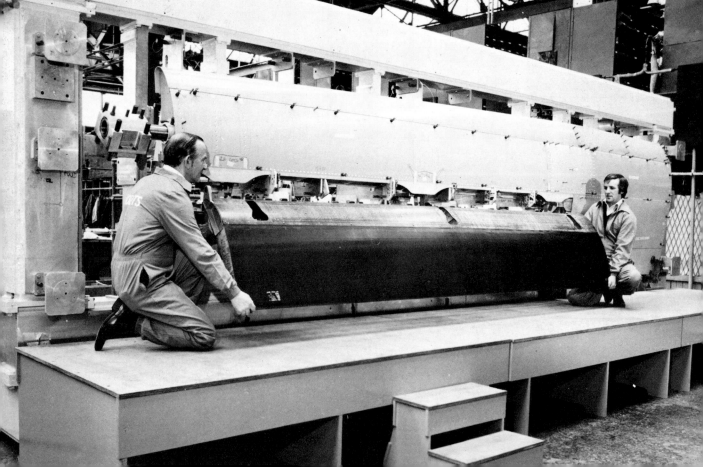

America, specialising in jet engine nacelles. Partners in this field are Boeing, Lockheed and Pratt & Whitney in the USA and British Aerospace, Fokker BV and Rolls-Royce in Europe, and the Shorts contribution ranges from relatively small airframe parts to complete wings. Some contracts call for a significant design effort: for instance, Shorts is a risk-sharing partner with Fokker BV in the F.28 Fellowship programme, with responsibility for wing design and production. The company also designs and manufactures the wings for the new Fokker 100 fanjet airliner. All the inboard trailing-edge flap assemblies for the Boeing 757 airliner, as well as engine nacelle components, are made by Shorts. The 757 wing flap in production at Belfast incorporates a 4m (13ft) long carbon-fibre section. In addition to supplying all the main landing gear doors for the Boeing 747, Shorts produces nacelle components for the Rolls-Royce RB.211-powered version of the aircraft.

Wings for the Fokker F.28. *(Shorts)*

Since winning its first contract for nacelle components in 1968 Shorts has expanded this side of its activities into a major programme. The company's research teams have made useful contributions to nacelle development, particularly in the areas of noise attenuation, thrust reversal and the application of new materials such as carbon-fibre composites. The nose cowls for the RB.211s which power all Lockheed Tri-Star airliners were manufactured by Shorts, and the company's current order book includes nacelle components for RB.211s on the Boeing 747 and 757 and complete nacelles for the BAe 146 feederliner's Avco-Lycoming ALF502Rs. Shorts was also selected to design and build the first flight test nacelle for the advanced Pratt & Whitney PW2037 turbofan developed for the Boeing 757.

Some very significant new partnerships were announced at the 1984 Farnborough Show. Shorts is to work with Sikorsky of the United States on a version of the S-70A Black Hawk to meet the RAF's AST 404 requirement. The British company would assemble, flight-test and deliver these tactical transport helicopters to the RAF and would also build complete fuselage sections for incorporation on the main production line

at Stratford, Connecticut. The companies will also exchange composite technology, and there is a plan to collaborate on future helicopter projects.

Partnered by another US company, Rohr Industries, Shorts is to offer an advanced nacelle for the new V2500 turbofan now being developed by the five-nation International Aero Engines AG to meet the requirement of future 150-seat jet airliners. The proposal covers all nacelle components and engine build-up. Shorts will be responsible for nose cowls and fan cowl doors, and will produce the systems for engine build-up, while Rohr will carry out final assembly.

Shorts displayed the 1,000th RB.211 nose cowl at Farnborough. Designed for the latest production RB.211, the 535E4 for the Boeing 757, the cowl has an all-carbon-fibre outer skin that is said to be 25% lighter than a comparable light alloy component. It is advances like this that assure Ulster's own aerospace company a place aboard some of the world's leading civil aircraft programmes.

US Army Sikorsky Black Hawks. Shorts and the American company are offering a Black Hawk variant in response to the RAF's AST.404 requirement for a tactical transport helicopter. *(Sikorsky)*

Shorts and Rohr Industries are working together on an advanced nacelle system for the new V2500 turbofan.

Opposite: **Apache on the warpath, carrying four Hellfire missiles, two rocket packs and an underfuselage swivel-mounted Hughes 30mm Chain Gun. The US Army requires several hundred examples of the Apache, which is probably the most survivable of all current dedicated attack helicopters.** *(Hughes Helicopters)*

Apache's rivals on the warpath

Elfan ap Rees

Apache, Hughes' heavyweight attack helicopter, begins 1985 with the first examples in US Army service and production building up to meet a stated demand for 515 aircraft between now and 1988. At between $9 and $12 million a copy the AH-64A Apache is hardly cheap. But the US Army considers it good value for money for it plugs a gap in the American arsenal that has persisted since the mid-1960s. Apache is mean: a day/night all-weather tankbuster with impressive nap-of-the-earth performance and a highly sophisticated avionics and weapons system, it is designed to plunge into the thick of the battle and survive.

Prime armament is 8-16 laser-guided Rockwell Hellfire anti-armour missiles and a swivel-mounted 30mm Hughes Chain Gun, while the stub wings can carry a variety of other missiles, rockets and podded weaponry. The Martin Marietta TADS/PNVS gives the pilot all-weather and night vision and targeting, and is linked to an integrated helmet and display system that allows the crew to aim and fly using a combination of head movements and monocle-presented symbology.

Though all this means that Apache is probably the most advanced combat helicopter in the world, it is now a decade since it first flew, and technology and attitudes are changing. New rotor systems, composite fuselage sections, and cathode ray tube instrument displays integrated with computerised cockpit management systems are now becoming more widely available, with the result that the AH-64A is no longer as far ahead of the game as it used to be.

Money is also in shorter supply, and many possible export customers simply cannot afford the number of Apaches it would need to make a purchase worthwhile. There is also the argument that three or four small, cheap helicopters could be bought for the price of one AH-64 and are more useful. Apache protagonists counter with the assertion that one AH-64 will survive longer than and do the work of six or seven smaller and less capable types, as well as demanding far fewer trained crewmen. Meanwhile, there are now available several Apache competitors, all of them cheaper and some very nearly as effective.

Since almost any helicopter these days can be turned into a gunship simply by hanging weapons on it, it is necessary to draw up a shortlist of true Apache rivals. Out go all the light single-engined types and the various troop transports. This leaves two categories: the side-by-side-seat multi-role types such as the Aérospatiale SA.365M, MBB BO 105, Sikorsky H-76 and Westland Lynx 3, and dedicated tandem-seat gunships like the Agusta A129 and the Bell SuperCobra. The Franco-German PAH-2 also falls into the latter category, but is too far in the future to be a serious rival much before the turn of the century.

Opposite: **Apache prototype fires Hellfire trials round.** *(Hughes Helicopters)*

Below: **Artist's impression of a naval version of the Apache, configured for shipboard operation and armed with four Harpoon anti-shipping missiles and two air-to-air Sidewinders.** *(Hughes Helicopters)*

Above: **Bell's AH-1T+ SuperCobra demonstrator.**
(Bell)

Above left: **Apache firing 2.75in folding-fin rockets from the 19-round pods mounted on its outboard pylons.** *(Hughes Helicopters)*

Left: **Hovering "hull-down" behind cover, Apache trials crew awaits details of their next target. Concealment tactics of this kind would be vital to survival on the battlefield.** *(Hughes Helicopters)*

Both of these categories are capable of carrying potent anti-armour weaponry integrated with advanced avionic and sensor systems. But Apache is a highly manoeuvrable helicopter with a weapon fit optimised for a single task: killing tanks. This rules out the multi-role types, leaving just the A129 Mangusta and the AH-1T-Plus SuperCobra.

The latter is the latest member of the highly successful and long-running Bell Cobra family, over 1,800 of which have been ordered in various versions since the original prototype first flew in 1965. AH-1T Plus introduces twin General Electric T700 engines to the basic US Marine Corps version of the Cobra. The resulting increase in power to 2,423kW (3,250shp) is matched by a weapons system upgraded to include new anti-armour missiles such as the Rockwell Hellfire, and the

addition of TADS/PNVS and new avionics. Also available as an option is a four-bladed composite rotor system based on that developed for the Bell 412 and now flying regularly on a Cobra in service with the Bell test fleet.

So by selecting the right package customers can put together a worthwhile facsimile of the Apache which, while it may fall short in some areas, nevertheless represents a cheaper alternative which is available today.

Available tomorrow (circa 1987) is the Agusta A129, potentially the Apache's biggest rival in the export market. Powered by two 682kW (915shp) Rolls-Royce Gem 2 engines, the Mangusta may appear at first sight to be a scaled-down Apache. But, as usual, looks are deceptive. In fact the Italian contender incorporates a Harris digital integrated multiplex cockpit management system which controls and monitors all the avionics, weapons, powerplant, electrical and utility systems, thus easing crew workload and allowing them to concentrate on the mission. Six Hellfire or eight TOW missiles can be carried, and a mast-mounted sight, full TADS/PNVS, and an integrated helmet and display sighting system are all incorporated.

The smaller size of the A129 should make it more manoeuvrable and less vulnerable than the heavyweight AH-64. In addition, Agusta argues that tolerance of 12.7mm strikes is likely to be all that is

Agusta A129 Mangusta, the first of Western Europe's dedicated attack helicopters. *(Agusta)*

needed on the battlefield, and that armouring the aircraft against 23mm shells results in avoidable cost and weight penalties. Only a real conflict could prove the point, but meanwhile the Italian Army is already convinced and has ordered 66 A129s, with an option on 30 more.

With attack helicopter markets in the Middle East, Asia and South America opening up, there are opportunities for all three competitors. US Government aid may give Bell and Hughes the edge in some quarters, particularly the Far East and certain South American countries. But Agusta has a high reputation in the Middle East and Argentina. The attack helicopter sales battle promises to be almost as fierce as anything these aircraft may have to fight for real.

Soviet Navy joins carrier big league

Robert Hutchinson

Sometime in 1994 the Soviet Navy will have its first nuclear-powered aircraft carrier (CVN) in operational service. This mighty ship, the first of as many as eight and carrying around 60 fixed-wing interceptor/strike aircraft, could prove a formidable adversary for the US Navy's carrier battle groups (CBGs). By the end of the century Moscow could therefore have a maximum of 480 supersonic, highly manoeuvrable combat warplanes at sea, a development that in the event of hostilities would lead to carrier battles far fiercer and more extensive than the great Second World War engagements in the Pacific. In peacetime the CVNs, perhaps accompanied by one or other of the *Kirov*-class nuclear

battlecruisers, attendant escorts and one or more amphibious landing ships, would be extremely potent instruments of power projection worldwide.

New US intelligence assessments of the 75,000-ton carrier indicate that the Soviets have speeded up work on the hull, code-named Black Com 2 by NATO, in the *Kiev*-class dock at Nikolayev Shipyard 444 on the Black

Heading picture: **Artist's impression of the new Soviet CVN now under construction on the Black Sea. Note the Flanker all-weather counter-air fighters on the flight deck, the two aircraft lifts and the six arrester wires.** *(US Defence Department)*

119

Artist's impression, based on reconnaissance satellite photographs, of the new CVN under construction at Nikolayev shipyard. Visible left in the fitting-out area is the fourth *Kiev*-**class carrier,** *Kharkov. (US Defence Department)*

Sea. The keel plates were laid down early in 1983 and already work is beginning on the ship's island superstructure. This would seem to indicate a high degree of priority for the 335m (1,100ft) long carrier, perhaps dictated by the desire of Admiral of the Fleet of the Soviet Union Sergei Gorshkov not only to see the carrier completed before his retirement but also to safeguard the programme against attempts to reduce naval expenditure by other arms of the Soviet armed forces.

The Yakovlev Forger VTOL aircraft, seen on the flight decks of the three (soon to be four) commissioned *Kiev*-class carriers, will not appear on the CVNs. This is for reasons of philosophy rather than because of disquiet over the less than satisfactory performance of this aircraft. Forger-A was believed originally to suffer great stability and safety problems when taking off with forward speed over the deck, and few, if any, Western observers have seen Forger in a fuel-saving STOL

take-off of the kind routinely practised by the British Harrier and US AV-8; payload range must therefore be severely limited. However, there have been recent suggestions, prompted by an article in the Polish magazine *Morze*, that the designation Yak-36MP for current Forgers is incorrect, referring only to the first 12 experimental VTOL-only testbeds, which were not fitted with either the auxiliary engine intake doors or the parallel dorsal fences either side of the lift engine intakes. The latest Forgers, said to be designated Yak-38, may in fact have a STOL capability.

Moving into the CVN league will bring the Soviets into direct competition with the US Navy's enormously capable carrier air groups, and so they require high-performance aircraft for the new carriers. It is known that tests with a full-scale CVN angled flight deck laid out in concrete and complete with arrester wires have been going on for three to four years at an air base "in the Black Sea area". This is not to say that the Soviets will be ready to embark the aircraft on board the new CVN, apparently called *Kremlin*, and immediately display a degree of operational expertise. Any navy pilot will testify that flying off and returning to a heaving deck is a far from simple business. Although the Soviet

USAF F-15s and RF-4C fly over the Soviet VTOL carrier *Minsk* in the Pacific. *(USAF)*

Navy has put a great deal of effort into monitoring flying operations from Western carriers, this is no substitute for practical experience. That is why *Kremlin* is not expected to become fully operational until some time in 1994 (some intelligence assessments put it two years earlier) after beginning sea trials in 1988-89.

Contrary to some reports, the Sukhoi Su-24 Fencer will not operate from the CVN. Initially, it is believed, a navalised variant of the MiG-23 Flogger will be carried by *Kremlin*. Later she will have the new Sukhoi Su-27 Flanker all-weather counter-air aircraft. This assumption is based on a Pentagon artist's impression of the carrier, published in *Jane's Defence Weekly*, which clearly shows Flanker (and a two-seat version)

Forger-A hovers over *Kiev* in the Atlantic. *(Royal Navy)*

Recent view of the third *Kiev*-class carrier
Novorossiysk in the Atlantic. There are seven
Forger-As on deck; that nearest the camera carries
two multiple rocket packs on underwing stations. The
Helix helicopter at the forward end of the deck
probably acts as a planeguard during flying
operations.

on the flight deck. Also visible are three steam catapults
and two deck lifts, one abaft the superstructure and the
other aft of the island on the starboard side.

Flanker, believed to be in series production at Kom-
somolsk in the Soviet Far East, will be armed with eight
beyond-visual-range AA-10 radar-homing missiles.
Flanker maximum speed is estimated at Mach 2.5 at
altitude and Mach 1.1 at sea level. Combat radius is
likely to be about 1,150km (715 miles), offering fair
intercept capability and loiter time on combat air patrol. The two engines, thought to be the same as the
MiG-31 Foxhound's, each develop 137.3kN (30,865lb
st) with afterburning.

Flanker was first spotted at the Soviet flight test
centre at Ramenskoye and given the US provisional
designation Ram-K. It was identified as having a look-
down/shoot-down weapon system and a possible secondary ground attack role. Initial operational capability in 1985 has been suggested by US intelligence
sources, but production problems may well delay this.
These difficulties include a shortage of engines, snags
with the aircraft's ECM package, and the lack of an

adequate on-board digital computer. Certainly the
Soviets are attempting a quantum jump in technology
with Flanker and the MiG-29 Fulcrum — the latter
programme has been hit by difficulties with the
pulse-Doppler radar — at a time when they are reckoned to be a long way behind the West in a number of
fields, particularly powerplants. Production "mis-
matches" — shortages of crucial sub-systems — should
therefore come as no surprise. Priority may have been
given to the MiG-31 Foxhound, which is now entering
service in increasing numbers. About four or five full
air-defence regiments, including one recently based in
East Germany, now have this Mach 2.4 aircraft.

Air wing on the new CVN will probably total 75
aircraft, including 15 Kamov Ka-27 Helix ASW
helicopters. There also seems to be no reason why the
Soviet Navy should not follow the Royal Navy down
the path of organic helicopter-borne AEW. As the
British found in the Falklands War, a carrier without
airborne early warning is at a great disadvantage, and
the Soviet Navy would find itself dangerously short of
operational options if it had to rely on shore-based
early-warning aircraft. Helicopters would not only give
the Soviet commander greater flexibility but also more
space in his below-deck hangar. It should therefore
come as no surprise if a Soviet version of the Westland
Sea King AEW, with its maritime surveillance radar in
an inflatable "kettledrum" container, makes its debut
within the next few years.

Tornado gathers strength

Bill Gunston

By autumn 1984 the number of Tornado multi-role attack aircraft delivered to the four initial customers had reached 360, with another 449 to go. The initial programme has been a tremendous success, but as this was written in September 1984 not one Tornado had been sold to a customer outside the three original partner countries. What then are the export and development prospects for the most important military aircraft in Western Europe?

It is important to remember that the most aggressive and capable sellers of defence hardware in the West, the USA and France — both of which unite their industry, armed forces and diplomatic service in the selling effort — have both been bitter opponents of the Tornado programme. Neither has lost any opportunity to assert that it is "a camel — a horse designed by a committee" and also desperately expensive. They have had remarkable success, especially because the media in Britain (and to a lesser degree in Federal Germany and Italy) are only too eager to print any story that appears controversial, or to knock an important high-technology product. As a result many people, including potential customers, believe that Tornado is as mediocre as it is costly.

Panavia has had to fight a rearguard action to try to

Heading picture: **Four of Marinefliegergeschwader 1's sea and coastal strike Tornados.** *(MBB)*

explain the truth about costs, which are in fact startlingly low and closer to prediction than on any other Western combat aircraft programme except possibly the F-16. The delivered price has kept just under the predicted (contractual) curve, while of the total 137.4% cost escalation in the past 14 years, 119.5% was due to inflation and only 17.9% to a real growth. Of this 17.9%, almost all was accounted for by growth in aircraft capability and new configurations requested by customers.

Indeed, one of the many impressive things about this great weapon system is the way its capability has been updated, month by month, to meet each new threat. All this was programmed in at the start. The four original customers in three countries have as far as possible agreed common updates, such as Mk 103 engines, a new electronic multiplexed (EMUX) data bus using all-digital signalling, active jammer and dispenser payloads, and new weapons such as Harm, Alarm and Sea Eagle. Several further updates or additions are being discussed, as well as the completely revised ECM and reconnaissance (ECR) version.

With 360 aircraft in service and well over 100,000 hours flown, Tornado is a mature weapon. The initial operators, apart from the big Tornado Tri-national Training Establishment (TTTE), where all Tornado aircrew from all four operators do their type conver-

Left: **IDS Tornados of the Italian Air Force's 6° Stormo Caccia-Bombardieri**.

Below left: **RAF's Tornado F2 interceptor in pale grey camouflage and carrying four Sky Flash and two Sidewinder missiles plus auxiliary fuel tanks.** (MoD)

Below: **Tornado in Luftwaffe camouflage at the Weapon Conversion Unit (WaKo) at Erding near Munich.** (Panavia)

**Tornados from the Trinational Training
Establishment**. *(BAe)*

sion, are the following: RAF, Tornado Weapons Con-
version Unit (TWCU) and Nos 9, 15, 16, 20, 27, 31 and
617 Sqns; Luftwaffe, JaboG 38 wing at Jever (the
weapons conversion unit), JaboG 31 at Nörvenich and
JaboG 32 at Lechfeld; Marineflieger, MFG 1 wing at
Jagel (Schleswig), to be followed by MFG 2 at
Eggebek; and Aeronautica Militare Italiana, 154°
Gruppo at Ghedi and 156° Gruppo at Gioia del Colle.

There is a fair amount of discussion between friendly
aircrew the world over, and by now the word has got
round that Tornado is enormously impressive and
popular.

Until November 1984 it was difficult to back up this
knowledge with fact, but once the RAF sent Tornados
to participate in the USAF Prairie Vortex bombing
competition there was no further argument. The four
aircraft from 617 Sqn, by a wide margin the smallest
aircraft taking part and the only ones to use flight
refuelling on contest missions, ran up scores that can

only be described as fantastic. They took first and second places in the top Le May Trophy (crew with most aggregate points from two high and low-level sorties), first and third in the John C. Meyer Trophy (non-B-52 crew with maximum low-level damage expectancy over two sorties), and second in the Mathis Trophy (best high and low-level team bombing scores, including time control, over four sorties). They beat B-52Gs and Hs of SAC, FB-111As of SAC, various F-111s of TAC and F-111Cs of the RAAF.

Air forces all over the world have kept careful watch on the way Panavia has developed Tornado on schedule and then delivered a steady nine aircraft per month with progressively increasing capability. For several years past the original customers have been discussing follow-on purchases with Panavia. The RAF is well satisfied with the existing Interdictor strike (IDS) version, which it designates the Tornado GR1 (for ground attack and reconnaissance, though in fact it also has an

Tornado GR1s symbolise the new shape of RAF air power during rehearsals for the Queen's birthday flypast.

important anti-ship attack capability using Sea Eagle or other missiles). The RAF has been negotiating for an additional production batch made up of both IDS aircraft and the new Air Defence Variant (ADV), called Tornado F2 by the RAF and so far a purely British development.

Federal Germany's Luftwaffe has been the chief sponsor of Tornado ECR, which is based on the IDS airframe. This could carry the full range of IDS weapons, though the two 27mm guns would be removed. The lower forward fuselage would house an advanced emitter-locator system, with flush receiver aerials in the wing glove leading edges. Further aft in the fuselage is room for two infra-red (IR) sensors, one a stabilised forward-looking infra-red (FLIR) with an auto-tracking mode for use as a precision detector of targets ahead or to either side, with a secondary role as a bad-weather or night visual aid to the pilot. The other is an IR linescan reconnaissance system. These and many other sensors would all feed new cockpit displays for pilot and weapon systems officer. Harm (High-speed Anti-Radar Missile) would be one of the weapon options. Italy is at the planning stage with a further Tornado batch which will almost certainly include the ECR version.

Exports beyond the three partner countries have until recently been held back by the extremely restrictive policies of the Federal German Government. Any attempt at overt selling has been taboo, but during the past 18 months discussions have been held with other NATO nations, and at the time of writing they were still continuing with Greece and Turkey (though Tornado was eliminated from a shortlist published by the former). Panavia is also talking to Japan, which has an important requirement for aircraft in this class, though for various political reasons it is almost impossible for that country to buy defence equipment from countries other than the USA.

More important in the near term is Saudi Arabia. Panavia has had no dealings with this Arab country, negotiations having been handled entirely by the British Government. At the time of writing a major contract had been in the process of refinement for many months, and should signatures be obtained the aircraft would be assembled in Britain, with British Aerospace also managing service support as part of an extension of the large existing collaboration between Warton and the Royal Saudi Air Force.

There has been long-standing irritation in Saudi Arabia at the refusal of the US Congress and State Department to sanction the supply of Fast Packs (conformal fuel/weapon pallets) for Saudi F-15 Eagles, which in consequence are restricted essentially to a purely defensive role. The requirement is thus for a multi-role interdiction/reconnaissance aircraft with a greater operating radius, and the IDS Tornado fills the bill admirably. The contract is likely to be for two batches of 20 each, to a build standard closely similar to that of the RAF GR1.

Negotiations between British Aerospace and the Sultanate of Oman have also been reported. No comment is forthcoming from Panavia or BAe, though at the 1984 Farnborough Show a senior Panavia manager went so far as to say: "If British Aerospace are talking with Oman, I can confirm there would be no objection by the Bonn government to a future contract." Unofficial reports claim that the Sultan of Oman's Air Force (SOAF) is eager to deploy the Tornado ADV in a form almost identical to the RAF Tornado F2. This aircraft has many major advantages over all of its competitors, and is also highly flexible in both the defensive and offensive roles. It has been suggested that the SOAF requirement is for two batches of eight aircraft each, forming a perfect partnership with the existing Jaguar attack force.

Panavia managing director Hans-Joachim Klapperich said at Farnborough that there were various other export possibilities, with differing timescales. Pressed to be more explicit, he suggested that Panavia could see the possibility of selling 150 aircraft over the next five years. This would be extremely useful, but to avoid too great a fall-off in workload at Warton, and at MBB and Aeritalia, it is clearly important to press ahead with the next-generation European Fighter Aircraft.

Jane's Jubilees

In this new-style Jubilees section the *Review* highlights Shorts and Hughes Helicopters, which in 1984 celebrated their 75th and 50th anniversaries respectively.

Shorts

1909 In January Short Brothers received its first order, for a pusher biplane for Francis K. McClean.

In February work began on construction of the first British purpose-built aircraft factory, at Shellbeach, Isle of Sheppey. This was opened in March.

A contract covering the production of six Wright Model A biplanes was signed by Wilbur Wright. The company thus became the first to put an aeroplane into series production.

On September 27, Biplane No 2 became the first Short Brothers powered aeroplane to fly.

1911 The Triple Twin, the first twin-engined aircraft from Short Brothers, flew on September 18.

1912 On January 10 Lt Charles Rumney Samson took off in Short S.38 from a specially built wooden platform on board HMS *Africa* to become the first British pilot to fly from a ship.

On May 9 Samson took off from HMS *Hibernia* to become the first pilot to fly from a ship under way.

1914 On July 27 Shorts test pilot Gordon Bell used S.84 for the first launch of a standard naval torpedo from an aeroplane.

Cdr Samson takes off from HMS *Hibernia*.

1915 On August 12 Flt Cdr C. H. Edmonds RNAS, flying a Short Admiralty Type 184 from HMS *Ben-My-Chree*, carried out the first air attack with a torpedo, sinking a Turkish supply ship in the Sea of Marmara during the Dardanelles campaign.

1916 A Short Admiralty Type 184, flown from HMS *Engadine* by Flt Lt Rutland and with Assistant Paymaster Trewin as observer, shadowed German warships on May 31 during the Battle of Jutland. This was the first successful use of a British aeroplane in a naval engagement.

1918 In August the first Short rigid airship flew as the R31.

1920 On August 20 the first all-metal Short aircraft, the Silver Streak (formerly Swallow), made its first flight.

Shorts' all-metal Silver Streak. *(Shorts)*

First Calcutta for Imperial Airways. *(Shorts)*

1921 The first Short-designed flying boat, the N.3 Cromarty, made its maiden flight on April 19.

1924 The first Short flying boat with an all-metal hull flew for the first time on November 7 as the S.1 Cockle.

1928 The first S.8 Calcutta commercial flying boat for Imperial Airways (G-EBVG) made its maiden flight on February 15.

1932 The S.14 Sarafand first flew on June 30. It was at that time the second largest aeroplane in the world, exceeded in size only by the far less successful Dornier DoX.

1936 In June Short Brothers & Harland Ltd was formed as a result of an agreement between Short Brothers (Rochester and Bedford) Ltd and the shipbuilders Harland & Wolff Ltd to build both land and marine aircraft in Belfast, Northern Ireland.

On July 3 S.23 *Canopus*, the first of Shorts' famous C-class Empire flying boats, made its maiden flight.

1937 The prototype Sunderland military flying boat first flew on October 16.

1938 During October 6-8 Short S.20 *Mercury*, the upper component of the Short-Mayo composite, set a world record, still unbeaten, for distance in a straight line by a seaplane. After being air-launched, it achieved 9,652km (5,997.5 miles).

1941 Short Stirling bombers of No 7 Sqn carried out the first RAF heavy bomber attack of the Second World War on the night of February 10/11, striking Rotterdam.

1951 The first Short S.A.4 Sperrin jet bomber prototype flew on August 10. Designed to the first

---

Short-Mayo composite, comprising the flying boat *Maia* **and the seaplane** *Mercury.*

The two Sperrin jet bomber prototypes. *(Shorts)*

British specification for a four-engined jet bomber, the Sperrin was the second such type to fly (the first was the Vickers Valiant).

1958 The first fixed-wing VTOL aeroplane to be built in the UK, the Short S.C.1, achieved its first free vertical take-off on October 25.

1963 The prototype S.C.7 Skyvan STOL utility light transport made its initial flight on January 17.

1981 The latest Shorts twin-turboprop commuter airliner, the 360, first flew as a prototype (G-ROOM) on June 1.

Short S.C.1 in vertical flight. *(Shorts)*

Hughes H-1 racer.

Hughes Helicopters

1934 Howard Hughes launched the aircraft division of the Hughes Tool Company on 14 February

1935 The Hughes H-1 racer, designed by Dick Palmer, established a world speed record for landplanes at 567.026km/hr (352.334mph) on September 13

1940 Work began on a new Hughes facility in Culver City, California. The aircraft company moved to this location from a leased hangar in Burbank.

1942 Hughes completed a major extension of its Culver City plant to accommodate assembly of the HK-1 flying boat. The structure covered more than four acres, making it one of the largest wooden buildings ever built.

1947 The Hughes H-4 Hercules flying boat, built at a reported cost of more than $22 million, was launched on November 1. Piloted by Howard Hughes himself, it made its one and only flight on the following day, covering about 1.6km (1 mile) across Los Angeles harbour at an altitude of 21-24m (70-80ft). The remarkable eight-engined H-4 remains the largest aircraft ever built, with a wing span of 97.536m (320ft).

1952 The Hughes XH-17 Flying Crane heavy-lift helicopter made its maiden flight on October 23. The first helicopter programme undertaken by Hughes, the XH-17 had the largest rotor ever to be fitted to a helicopter, at 37.62m (130ft) diame-

The XH-17 experimental heavy-lifter had the largest rotor ever fitted to a helicopter.

XV-9A hot-cycle research helicopter.

---

ter. In 1953 the XH-17 flew at a gross weight of more than 22,680kg (50,000lb).

1956 The Model 269, the predecessor of the TH-55A and Model 300 helicopters, made its first flight as a prototype in October.

1963 The OH-6A Cayuse, military predecessor of the Model 500 helicopter, made its first flight on February 27.

1964 The XV-9A Hot Cycle helicopter, built under US Army contract for research into the hot-cycle propulsion system, first flew in November.

1966 The OH-6A established 23 world records for helicopters, for speed, distance and altitude. Eighteen still stand. Among these was distance in a straight line in Class E.1, set on April 6-7 at 3,561.55km (2,213 miles).

1973 The first Hughes XM230 Chain Gun automatic cannon was fired. It was the first of a new line of Hughes Helicopters ordnance products.

1975 The Hughes Model 500D first flew in production form on October 9.

The first YAH-64 Apache attack helicopter prototype flew on September 30.

1976 The Apache was named as winner of the US Army's Advanced Attack Helicopter programme.

1981 On December 17 Hughes' revolutionary NOTAR (No Tail Rotor) helicopter flew for the first time.

The revolutionary NOTAR helicopter, based on an Army OH-6 Cayuse. *(Hughes Helicopters)*

The AH-64 Apache is currently Hughes' biggest military programme. *(Hughes Helicopters)*

1982 Ground was broken in March for Hughes' Apache Assembly and Flight Test Centre in Mesa, Arizona. The facility became operational and was dedicated in December. The main assembly building has an area of 22,575m² (243,000 sq ft).

1983 Hughes delivered its 1,000th M242 25mm automatic cannon to the US Army in August.

1984 The first production Apache made its maiden flight.

Hughes Helicopters entered its second 50 years with a new parent company, the McDonnell Douglas Corporation.

Enter the thinking missile

Roy Braybrook

Many of the air-to-air and air-to-surface guided missiles now in use are either improved versions or derivatives of first-generation (post-war) weapons that entered service in the 1950s or 1960s. Although some types, such as the AIM-9L Sidewinder and AIM-54C Phoenix, are still remarkable products, most of these missiles have now reached the limits of their potential and are due for replacement. For instance, most existing air-to-air guided weapons have a single-stage guidance system that has to be locked on to the target before launch, is easily defeated by countermeasures, does not match the missile's aerodynamic range, and

places severe constraints on the parent aircraft's launch (and possibly post-launch) manoeuvring.

We are now seeing the leading edge of a new generation of air-launched missiles that will overcome such problems, making use of multi-stage guidance and new types of homing head, rocket motor, guidance equation, fuze and warhead. The latest avionics display a quantum advance in reliability, and missiles are becoming far more "intelligent". For example, the weapon

Heading picture: **Sea Eagle anti-shipping missile drops away from Buccaneer trials aircraft.** *(BAe Dynamics)*

135

may be able to compute the speed of the target and compare it with an acceptable velocity bracket in order to reject the sun and non-representative decoys. Rather than steering directly for the jetpipe nozzle, an infra-red-homing missile may now compute the position of the target's centre of mass and head straight for it. More efficient guidance systems are also making possible a reduction in minimum firing range. Combined with a general reduction in missile size and weight (and hence an increase in missile numbers per aircraft), this offers the prospect of short-range missiles finally replacing automatic cannon in dogfight use, although the gun may be retained as a back-up system and for its operational flexibility.

Air-to-air missiles

Most of the new guided weapons are based on emerging technologies, but there is one new category that continues to owe much to existing missiles. The idea of arming helicopters with lightweight air-to-air missiles for use against other helicopters is fast gaining acceptance, although it appears to be largely motivated by the suspicion that the laser-guided AT-6 Spiral used by the Mi-24 Hind-E has a secondary air-to-air role.

In general, existing air-to-air missiles are probably not suitable for helicopter use, since conventional fixed-wing launch speeds are needed during their boost phase. However, the AIM-9 appears to be an exception to this rule: 44 new Bell AH-1Ts for the USMC are to

be armed with this missile. The more usual approach to the problem is to adapt man-portable SAMs, such as the General Dynamics FIM-92 Stinger. France is developing the Matra AATCP Mistral for helicopter use, and there is interest elsewhere in using the command-guidance Shorts Blowpipe and the laser beam-riding Bofors RBS-70.

Short-range air-to-air missiles for fixed-wing use are almost invariably IR-homing, the resulting very small miss distances being reflected in the light weight of the warhead and hence of the complete weapon. In this class first-generation designs have proved capable of much development. The introduction of cooled homing heads that can acquire the relatively low-temperature gases of the target jetpipe plume have (when associated with improvements in manoeuvrability) made possible all-aspect attacks with missiles such as the AIM-9L and -9M, Matra Magic 2 and Rafael Python 3. Firings at large angles from the fuselage datum of the launch aircraft are in some cases made possible by slaving the homing head to the radar antenna or a helmet-mounted sight (HMS), as with the AIM-9L and South Africa's Kentron V3B Kukri.

First-generation missiles have come a long way from

ASRAAM, being developed jointly by Britain and West Germany, is a fire-and-forget air-to-air missile capable of all-aspect attacks at large off-boresight angles. *(BAe Dynamics)*

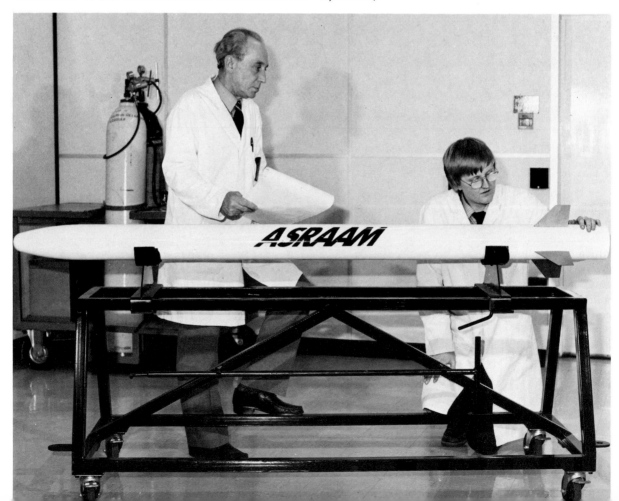

F-14 carrying an AMRAAM test round on its starboard forward fuselage station. *(Hughes)*

the original AIM-9B Sidewinder, but they still have serious restrictions, including a limited IR acquisition range (relative to aerodynamic range), and a tendency to be decoyed by flares and the sun and to be thrown off course completely by IR noise generators. Current IR homing heads are pointed very precisely at the target by passing its radiation through a "chopper" to produce a series of IR pulses, the frequency variation and phase of which correspond to angular pointing errors. Such a system may be useless if the target has countermeasures equipment producing random IR pulses. One possible solution is the IR-imaging focal plane array, which also eases target discrimination against a bright background (especially severe when using long wavelengths to detect the target's kinetically heated nose and leading edges) and facilitates in-flight acquisition. An imaging IR seeker is believed to be a feature of the Anglo-German Advanced Short-Range Air-Air Missile (ASRAAM), currently being developed by British Aerospace Bodenseewerk Geraetetechnik (BBG).

This new homing head will allow ASRAAM to exploit its full aerodynamic range potential, being launched on inertial guidance and searching for the target only in the terminal phase. Designed from the outset for the dogfight role, ASRAAM will have its target initially designated by an HMS, which will presumably be linked to the launch aircraft radar so that target trajectory can be computed and fed to the missile. Missile cruise speed will be very high, which explains ASRAAM's reliance on body lift rather than wings.

Two-stage guidance will also be built into the Matra *Missile d'Interception et de Combat* (MICA), which is intended to replace both the short-range Magic 2 and medium-range Super D. The new missile will have two alternative homing systems: an IR seeker and an active radar homing head.

In spite of the development effort currently being devoted to short-range AAMs, there is a swing in emphasis within NATO towards medium-range weapons. This appears to derive from the need to achieve a high kill ratio in the face of adverse odds. The problem can be solved only by an outstanding missile system that will outrange the enemy, leaving the short-range weapon only as a back-up. ASRAAM therefore seems unlikely to rival the production levels of the AIM-9, which it is to replace in certain applications.

Typical existing medium-range weapons are the latest AIM-7M Sparrow, and Sparrow derivatives such as the BAe Sky Flash and Selenia Aspide. Since they use semi-active radar homing the launch aircraft must continue to illuminate the target throughout missile flight, thereby exposing itself to short-range return fire. In principle, NATO air forces will replace Sparrow with the Hughes AIM-120 Advanced Medium-Range Air-Air Missile (AMRAAM), which has active radar terminal guidance. While permitting a rapid disengagement, AMRAAM also allows the launch aircraft to engage multiple targets simultaneously. If normal guidance is ruled out by radar jamming, AMRAAM can function in a home-on-jam mode.

To exploit AMRAAM's full aerodynamic range, up to three guidance modes may be employed in one firing. Immediately after launch against a manoeuvring target the missile would fly on inertial guidance, using update information transmitted from the fighter's fire-control system by data link. In the second phase the fighter could break away while the missile continued in an autonomous inertial mode. Finally, the missile would switch to active radar homing, using either a high pulse-repetition frequency (PRF) for a look-up target or a medium PRF in look-down mode. It has been reported that the second AMRAAM model (AIM-120B) will have passive terminal homing, but it is not clear whether this would be done on radar or IR wavelengths.

The use of weapons such as Sparrow has always been limited by target identification problems. Since IFF is unreliable, either the target must be identified visually (by the crew of another aircraft, for example) or the rules of engagement must allow firings without positive target identification. With AMRAAM and the even longer-range missiles of the future, the hope is that the radar of the launch aircraft will be able to provide non-co-operative target recognition (NCTR). Given a track-while-scan fighter radar, AMRAAM can be ripple-fired against four targets.

Since the early 1980s there have been reports of USAF and USN-funded studies of a very-long-range air-to-air missile making use of spaceborne IR sensors to detect hostile aircraft. Powered by a solid-fuel ducted ramjet, such a weapon would combine high speed with a range of around 185km (115 miles). One of

A Rockwell International Hellfire helicopter-launched anti-tank missile about to score a hit during tests. Hellfire achieved better than 90% accuracy in operational trials. *(Rockwell International)*

the Navy objectives is a missile much lighter than the 447kg (985lb) AIM-54, since the F-14 cannot make a carrier landing when loaded with six Phoenix. Extremely high radar power will confer a "burn-through-jamming" capability. The trend is illustrated by the fact that the AIM-54A used only 25W and a 28cm (11in) antenna, while AMRAAM transmits 300W from its 17.8cm (7in) dish.

Future lines of development include the use of hypersonic speeds, although this poses severe problems in the form of thermal shock to the radome or IR dome. In the event of a near-miss, most of the energy in a conventional warhead is wasted. Directed-energy warheads are much more effective, as long as the missile can be rolled to aim them at the target. Kinetic energy kills are also being studied, presumably with a view to destroying the pressure cabin and associated targets.

Long-range missiles such as the AIM-54 are believed to follow a high-altitude trajectory in order to minimise the energy wasted in overcoming aerodynamic drag. It therefore follows that an air-launched missile could have some capability against a satellite in low orbit, although the fighter would rely on ground control to achieve the required firing position.

The first air-launched anti-satellite (ASAT) missile is believed to have been a Martin Marietta Bold Orion rocket, fired from a B-47 against the Explorer 6 spacecraft over Cape Canaveral in 1959. Since that time the US has concentrated on surface-launch tests, using Nike Zeus and Thor boosters. The possibility of a far less expensive air-launched ASAT system has recently led to tests of a Vought air-launched miniature vehicle (ALMV) on an F-15, using a SRAM booster for the first stage and an Altair III rocket for the second. The complete missile is 5.2m (17ft) long and weighs 1,225kg (2,700lb). Reports indicate that it can attain a maximum altitude of 800km (500 miles). At the time of writing, ALMV testing against space targets has been delayed by Congressional action. If development is completed successfully, the USAF will modify 40 TAC F-15s to equip one squadron at Langley AFB, Virginia, and one at McChord AFB, Washington. It is believed that during 1968-78 the Soviet Union carried out 20 air-launched ASAT tests, of which roughly half were successful.

Air-to-surface missiles
Current developments in the air-to-surface field are perhaps less dramatic than those described above but they are nonetheless important.

At the lower end of the scale, current helicopter-launched anti-tank missiles are mostly based on semi-active command-to-line-of-sight (SACLOS) guidance, in which the operator holds a stabilised sight on the target and an IR sensor measures the angular displacement of the missile and initiates corrective signals. This

Mock-up of ALARM, the advanced anti-radar missile being developed for the RAF. *(BAe Dynamics)*

The ramjet-powered ANS anti-shipping missile is a French/West German project.

system appears to be a significant improvement over simple command guidance, but it exposes the helicopter to return fire and allows only one target to be engaged at a time. The new Rockwell AGM-114 Hellfire employs laser homing, so that a target designated by another source (on the ground or airborne) can be attacked from behind cover. Coding of the laser designators also allows four targets to be engaged simultaneously. Projected developments include millimetre-wave radar guidance for all-weather operation.

Laser homing is also employed by the AGM-65E USMC version of Maverick. The Vought Hypervelocity Missile (HVM) will be guided by signals transmitted by a laser beam, allowing multiple target engagements in a single pass. The warhead will be a depleted uranium rod or a hollow cylindrical cutter, striking at around 460m/sec (1,500ft/sec). An increasing number of missiles (eg, AGM-65D) are using imaging-IR guidance, which among other advantages permits an attack to be directed at the centre of a ship's waterline.

A great deal of effort is being applied to stand-off munitions dispensers as a means of attacking armour concentrations or runways. The general form for such weapons is a rectangular-section fuselage with flip-out wings and a rocket motor or turbine engine.

Another example of the growing intelligence of missiles is the ability of the latest anti-ship weapons (eg, BAe Sea Eagle) to select a particular vessel out of a group of ships. In the anti-radar category, missiles such as the General Dynamics AGM-78 Standard ARM can continue to a memorised target position if the transmitter shuts down. The BAe Air-Launched Anti-Radar Missile (ALARM) has a loiter mode in which it hangs on a parachute while searching for targets, having been prebriefed with a list of priorities.

In the long-range air-to-surface category, one of the main concerns is to minimise losses during penetration. Thus it is reported that the Aérospatiale ASMP (*air-sol moyenne portée*) missile has a cruise speed of Mach 3. The ramjet-powered MBB/Aérospatiale ANS (*anti-navire supersonique*) appears to have a similar capability. Looking further into the future, the General Dynamics Advanced Cruise Missile (ACM) is said to rely largely on stealth technology. The state of the art in air-launched guided weapons continues to advance at an impressive pace.

Big Three dominate world aerobatics

Don Berliner

Aerobatics, *voltige aérienne*, stunt flying: call it what you wish, this is one of the most demanding of all the aeronautical disciplines. It requires an aeroplane designed and built expressly for violent manoeuvring, and a pilot mentally and physically prepared to devote 100% to the achievement of absolutely round loops, nearly explosive flick rolls, and vertical climbs that do not deviate from the ideal by as much as five degrees.

Aerobatics can be the most solitary of flying activities, involving hour after hour of painstaking reduction of the tiniest of flaws to the point of invisibility. The only spectator is often an equally isolated aide on the ground, taking note of each tremor and hesitation so that his nit-picking report may lead to a better

Heading picture: **Hungarian pilot waves from his Zlin 50LA just before touchdown.** *(Don Berliner)*

141

next flight. The ultimate object of all this is admission to the glamorous and very public arena called the World Aerobatics Championships. There the loneliness of the sport gives way to a festival, with most of the world's aerobatic authorities staring intently at each manoeuvre, and a panel of ten judges recording every minute variation from perfection and taking great delight (so the pilots see it) in deducting points for the most unimportant and unintentional of errors.

Every two years the greatest devotees of the sport gather to place their skills and reputations on the line, in full expectation of winning the Aresti Cup (as men's individual champion) and the Nesterov Trophy (as men's team champions). The venue changes from one meeting to the next, for no country is willing to expend the necessary money and effort more than once a decade. In 1984 the host was Hungary and the location a spacious sport flying field near Bekescsaba in the far south-eastern corner of the country. Thirteen nations sent 48 men and 16 women, formed into ten men's teams and four women's.

Favourites, as they had been since 1970, were the Czechs, the Soviets and the Americans; each had won both major trophies in the past three championships.

The Czechs were led by 1983 European champion Petr Jirmus, the Soviets by reigning world champion Victor Smolin, and the Americans by two-time runner-up Henry Haigh and Australian Super Challenge winner Kermit Weeks.

The Czechs were equipped with the latest 224kW (300hp) version of their Zlin 50L; the Soviets had a pair of improved Yak-55s and two brand-new Sukhoi Su-26s, all with 268kW (360hp) radial engines; and the Americans had a gaggle of highly modified Pitts Special biplanes, the powerful Weeks "Solution" and the one-of-a-kind Haigh Super Star. Facing them was a programme of four quite different flights. The opening

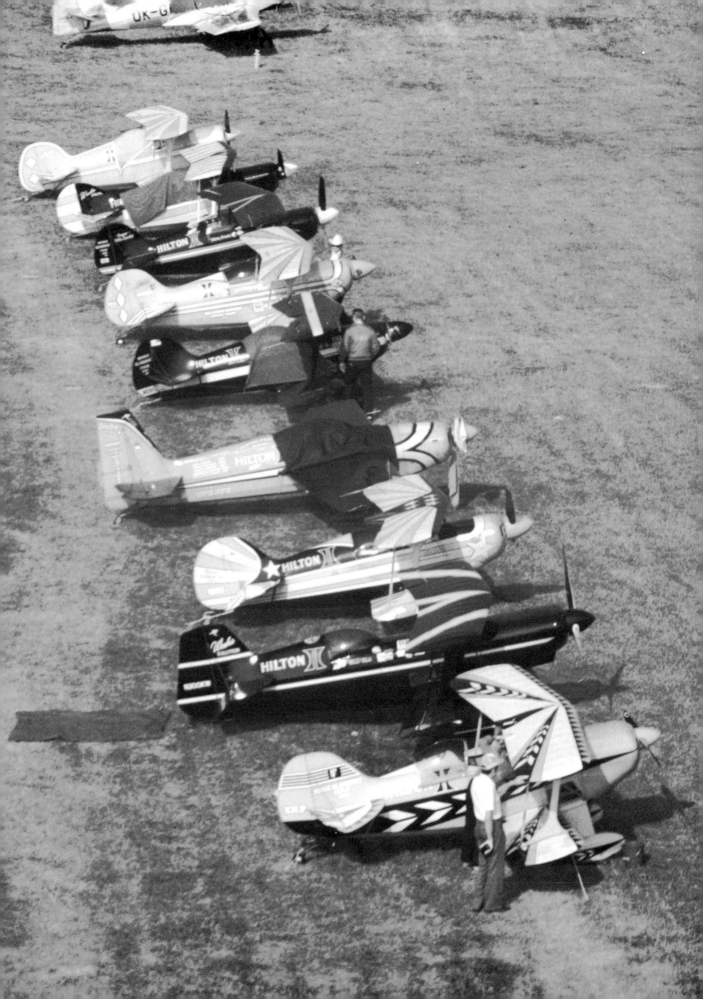

Above: **New Soviet Sukhoi Su-26, featuring wings and tail made of plywood and covered with fibreglass, improved downward visibility and high wing loading.** *(Don Berliner)*

Right: **New world champion Petr Jirmus.** *(Don Berliner)*

Below right: **West German pilot/designer Walter Extra sits on the wing of one of his new Extra 230 monoplanes. With him is America's Henry Haigh.** *(Don Berliner)*

Known Compulsory is a fixed sequence of 17 very difficult manoeuvres which each pilot had been practising since the start of the season. The Freestyle consists of 22 prescribed manoeuvres, combined by each pilot according to a complex set of rules and in keeping with his individual taste and skills. The Unknown Compulsory is created by the officials during the contest and they cannot be practised before it is flown for the judges. The final Four-minute Freestyle is a throwback to an earlier era which allows the pilots to ignore precision and perform any manoeuvres they wish, even inventing as they go.

At the 1984 event, regardless of the state of international tensions, the pilots, mechanics and fans mingled quite freely, exchanging technical notes and predictions. Many were old friends, all were members of the small, exclusive fraternity of aerobatics. The competition might be fierce, but with no prize money at stake — the only reward is prestige within a select community — no-one seemed ready to ignore sportsmanship and safety for the sake of winning.

So much in the way of points and instant stature rested on the opening sequence that the hands on stick and throttle must have been wet with sweat and far from steady. From the opening 1½ flick rolls during a 45° dive, to the finishing full vertical aileron rolls, the aeroplanes whirled from one corner of the 1,000-metre cube of air to the other. They tailslid, rolled around a circle, spun inverted. Their pilots pushed and pulled and strained against inescapable gravity. Wires whined and propellers screamed while the judges calmly and methodically announced their decisions. Through the point-heavy Freestyle the pilots charged, tackling even more manoeuvres of even greater difficulty. The

monoplanes were graceful, the biplanes violent, all were capable of the most extreme gyrations.

After the first round the Czech Jirmus and his men's team had a slim lead, while the American Linda Meyers surprised the favoured Soviet women's squad but was unable to carry her teammates with her. After the second Jirmus had consolidated his individual lead but the Americans had squeezed past his team by a few points. The Soviet women had, as expected, taken up a commanding position.

It was the Unknown that determined the team champions. The Americans flew through it without a single zeroed manoeuvre from the five of them — a highly meritorious achievement in this toughest of tests. The Czechs, on the other hand, had only Jirmus. Their other men erred frequently and allowed the American trio of Weeks, Haigh and Harold Chappell to fly away to a big victory and the Nesterov Trophy.

The Soviet women's team came through once again, even though its two former world champions, Leonova and Iakova, were a disappointment. Their team depth paid off, however, and they came away with the gold

Soviet Yak-55s (foreground) and Su-26s. To the right is chief mechanic Pyotr Pervushin. *(Don Berliner)*

medals. Not so the Soviet men, whose problems with their new aeroplanes were compounded by what looked like a lack of practice. The result was a showing reckoned to be their poorest in 20 years.

The final four-minute "air show" flight was again dominated by Kermit Weeks and his superb original-design biplane, though he failed to garner enough points to replace Jirmus in the winner's circle or West Germany's Manfred Stroosenreuther, flying a nearly identical Zlin, in second spot. The women's world champion was Khalide Makaganova of the USSR, followed by a Soviet teammate and American rookie Debby Rihn.

In the final accounting there were winners from three countries, and they flew both monoplanes and biplanes. Trends were hard to distinguish. New designs and new materials appeared but played roles which were far from decisive. It must be left for the next world championships — at Cranfield, England, in August 1986 — to reveal any clear new directions the sport may follow in the final years of this decade.

Letting the drone take the strain

Kenneth Munson

Ever since man first went into battle, commanders have sought better ways to obtain reliable combat intelligence that would allow them to deploy their forces more effectively. This need is more urgent than ever on the high-speed modern battlefield, and has led to a resurgence of interest in the agile, sophisticated and cost-effective tactical mini-RPV. To a large extent this reawakening has come about as a result of the use of such vehicles by the Israeli armed forces during the Lebanon campaigns of the last few years.

The value of remotely piloted vehicles was amply demonstrated to the United States forces during their long involvement in Vietnam, which ended in early 1973. Later that year, in the Middle East, the same lesson was learned by the armed forces of Israel during the Yom Kippur War. Yet 11 years later the United States — virtually the home of the RPV — had not one single operational type in its inventory, while Israel had

two, both highly successful: the IAI Scout and Tadiran Mastiff.

Israel's mini-RPVs, used on an unprecedented scale and with spectacular success in the Lebanon, have revolutionised the gathering of tactical intelligence. Following their early use to recce Syrian SAM sites in the Beka'a in 1981, their ability to loiter for up to seven hours and send back live TV pictures to battlefield commanders made them almost indispensable, and they saved the lives of countless artillery spotters, tank crews, infantrymen and pilots by providing advance warning of enemy defences and positions. It was widely reported, and not denied by the Israelis, that the Minister of Defence and the Chief of Military Intelligence

Heading picture: **The Mastiff Mk III tactical air reconnaissance/surveillance mini-RPV, produced by Israel's Tadiran.** *(Tadiran)*

Israel Aircraft Industries' Scout mini-RPV with its launch truck and mobile ground control station. *(IAI)*

each had a TV monitor in his office in order to keep up with the flow of data being relayed back by the RPVs.

Scout and Mastiff, both developed to specifications issued soon after the October 1973 war, typify the modern mini-RPV, having a launch weight in the 100-160kg (220-353lb) bracket, of which 30-40kg (66-88lb) constitutes the mission payload: TV or still cameras, or other sensors such as forward-looking infra-red (FLIR) or linescan, plus a data link and autopilot. Designed to operate in a hostile, electromagnetically active environment, they have a small visual cross-section which appears even smaller on the enemy's radar screens because much of their structure is made of non-radar-reflecting fibreglass or similar composite materials. Fitting an engine of modest power, with its exhaust gases dispersed by the pusher propeller, minimises the infra-red signature, and visual or radar detection is made even more difficult by an overall finish of non-reflective paint. It is not surprising that a similar twin-boom pusher layout has been adopted for a whole crop of other RPV designs, including Italy's Mirach-20, the British Aerospace Stabileye, Developmental Sciences' SkyEyes and a whole family from E-Systems in the USA.

The Israeli Army's success with its mini-RPVs is in sharp contrast to that of its American counterpart, which looks like having to wait until at least 1987 before its own battlefield RPV, the Lockheed Aquila (which was initiated at about the same time as Scout and Mastiff), becomes operational. Aquila is smaller than

the Israeli drones, with payload accounting for some 24kg (53lb) of its 113kg (249lb) launch weight. Funding deferments, difficulties in fitting the sophisticated onboard equipment into the tiny (2.08m, 6ft 10in-long) airframe, and repeated redefinition of the mission requirements have all played their part in stretching out the Aquila programme and increasing its cost. As a result, the US Army has decided to reduce its planned purchase from 995 vehicles to 548, while the other US services are looking at simpler ways of acquiring effective mini-RPVs: the Air Force with its Pave Tiger expendable drone, the Navy and Marine Corps by evaluating the Israeli Mastiff. The first USMC Mastiff unit was due to become operational by the end of 1984.

Nor is the US Goliath the only nation to take a leaf out of the Israeli David's book. Anyone seeking proof of a worldwide interest in miniature RPVs needs only to scan the list of more than 200 delegates from Australia, Belgium, Canada, West Germany, India, Israel, Italy, South Africa, Sweden, Switzerland, Syria, the UK and the USA who registered for the 4th International RPV Conference, held at Britain's Bristol University in April 1984. Belgium and Italy were among the first to employ mini-RPVs operationally. Sweden is now tacitly admitting its mistake in abandoning earlier experimental programmes and is hoping to close the gap by buying foreign systems and technology. Syria, of course, was on the receiving end of an effective drone campaign in the Lebanon.

RPVs are no longer the preserve of the richer or more technologically advanced countries. From Argentina come reports of the piston-engined Chimango (already exported to Iran, Peru and South Africa) and the transonic Bigua, under development for possible naval reconnaissance, while Brazil is developing the 93kg (205lb) BQM-1BR, also jet-powered, as its first multipurpose mini-RPV. The Northwestern Polytechnical University of Xian, in the Chinese People's Republic, is evaluating a camera-carrying piston-engined drone called the D-4, with a 30kg (66lb) payload and 140kg (309lb) launch weight. Although the first mini-RPV from India's Aeronautical Development Establishment in Bangalore was a failure (in 1976), a more successful experimental twin-boom pusher design which takes off at 70kg (154lb) (including 25kg, 55lb of payload and fuel) has since been produced. In 1984 the Establishment also began testing the Pilotless Target Aircraft (PTA), a larger, jet-powered vehicle intended for battlefield or other surveillance applications. Italy's Meteor SpA has developed the multi-role Andromeda system, which can use any one of a family of Mirach air vehicles, from the tiny 19.5kW (26hp), 150kg (331lb) Mirach-20 to the 1,000kg (2,205lb) Mach 0.92 Mirach-600 with two 3.34kN (750lb st) turbojet engines. The first all-Japanese RPV, a research vehicle for surveillance/reconnaissance missions, is under development by Fuji, with guidance systems, onboard TV camera and ground control equipment by other Japanese manufacturers. South Africa's National Dynamics has already exported its unique rhomboid-wing Eyrie (though *not* to Argentina, despite impassioned requests in 1982). Britain's AEL has developed its "model aircraft" Snipe III (already sold as a target in the Middle East and elsewhere) into the Sparrowhawk battlefield surveillance RPV, equipped with TV or still cameras and chaff/flare dispensers. Model aircraft hobbyist Ben Buckle is in on the act with his private-venture PR 21 homebuilt, which has already achieved some export success. Coming from a more established British manufacturer, Flight Refuelling's new Raven, described as "an unmanned aircraft applications demonstrator," is based on the XRAE series of experimental vehicles developed over a number of years by the Royal Aircraft Establishment.

In 1984, however, the most significant British project was the Army's Phoenix battlefield surveillance RPV. In some respects its history resembles that of the American Aquila, in that it began with an earlier prog-

China's camera-carrying D-4 is powered by a 22.5kW (30hp) piston engine.

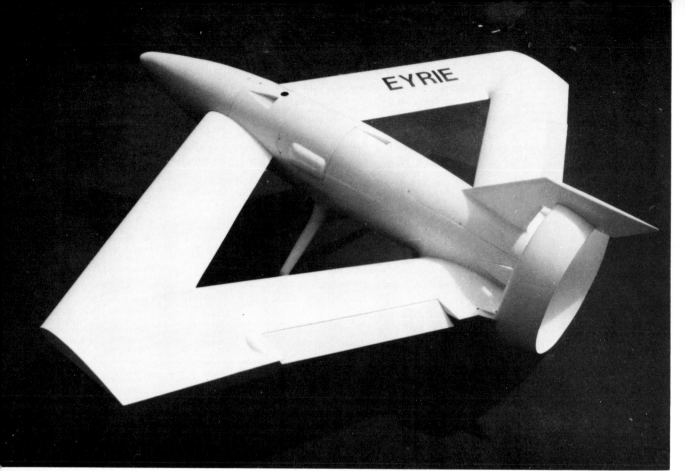

Above left: **The South African National Dynamics Eyrie has an all-composite rhomboid wing and a shrouded propeller. It can carry 36.5kg (80.5lb) of TV cameras or electronic warfare equipment.**

Left: **British private enterprise in the form of Ben Buckle's homebuilt PR 21.**

Above: **MBB's Tucan is booster-launched from either a ramp or a container. An anti-tank version is under development.**

Below: **Italy's Meteor Mirach-20 is an extremely compact mini-RPV designed for target acquisition/designation, battlefield surveillance and artillery fire adjustment.** *(Meteor)*

ramme (known as Supervisor) which priced itself out of existence because, as the Army now admits, the user "was allowed to become greedy". Wiser counsels have prevailed with Phoenix, for which a winning design unofficially emerged in late 1984 from entries by Ferranti/Slingsby and GEC Avionics/Flight Refuelling. Phoenix is a rapid-deployment system comprising air vehicles with thermal imaging (infra-red) cameras, a mobile ground control station and a remotely deployed ground data terminal. Several hundred RPVs are said to be required. They will be used for low-level scrutiny of targets or areas detected by higher-flying Castor (Corps Airborne Stand-Off Radar) reconnaissance aircraft and deemed worthy of closer and more detailed examination.

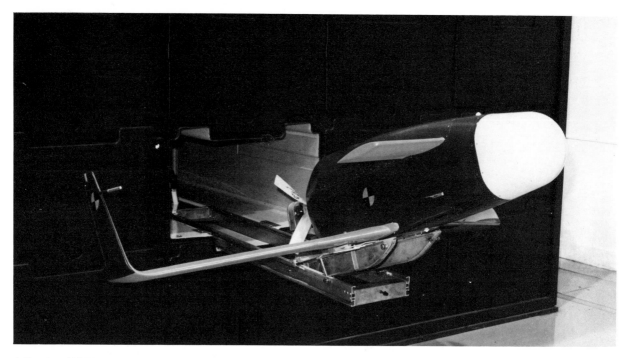

A Boeing YCGM-121A Pave Tiger deployed from its 15-drone "filing cabinet".

Apart from their obvious value in avoiding the unnecessary risking of human pilots (the US Navy, for example, offshore during the Lebanon crisis, had to expose its F-14 Tomcats for the overland reconnaissance role), RPVs are proving increasingly cost-effective for many missions as a result of improved manufacturing techniques, greater use of composite materials, and advances in electronics and miniaturisation of equipment. Military acceptance of RPVs is also widening, as witness Major-General New, Britain's Assistant Chief of the General Staff (Operational Requirements) in 1984: "The British military user is waiting most eagerly for his RPVs. They could have been used with great profit in the Falklands . . . It has become an urgent need for us as we develop the capabilities for deeper attack."

At least the same degree of eagerness is being shown by the US Air Force, which is to acquire the Boeing Pave Tiger expendable ECM and attack mini-RPV. This tiny (127kg/280lb, 1.78m/5ft 10in long) vehicle is a fire-and-forget drone which can carry up to 27kg (59.5lb) of equipment to jam enemy radars, or a non-nuclear warhead to attack selected targets. Up to 15 Pave Tigers can be transported and stored in a "filing cabinet" on individual zero-length launch rails; as the rails emerge from their compartments, the folded wings flip into flying position and the drones are launched by an electronically fired rocket booster. They can fly pre-programmed missions, or can be re-programmed by a tactical commander in the field to act, for example, as an "aerial minefield" in the face of enemy attack aircraft. Boeing claims that it could turn out one Pave Tiger vehicle every 20min. The USAF is expected to buy about 1,000 initially, but Boeing believes that sales could eventually run into six figures, and has already launched an export version known as the Brave 200.

Pave Tiger is simple, flexible, capable of rapid deployment, and quick and easy to produce. An entire 15-drone unit can be handled in the field by a two-man crew. Both it and Phoenix provide evidence that the US and Britain at least have learned that the greatest enemies of getting an effective mini-RPV system into operational service are cost escalation and delay. To quote General New again: "The user is determined not to be seduced into paying 90 per cent more money for the last 10 per cent capability, and you (the industry) must not allow us to do it. Above all, we must between us 'keep it simple'."

The Israelis have of course already absorbed that lesson. Having produced two first-class RPVs, they have recognised that Scout and Mastiff now have so much in common that the obvious next step is for their formerly competing manufacturers to join forces and collaborate on a single replacement vehicle. Applications for this new RPV are expected to include day and night reconnaissance, electronic warfare/ECM/decoy, communications relay, and laser target designation. The world's RPV design teams must already be wondering what new surprises the ever-ingenious Israelis have up their sleeves.

Fighting fly-by-wire

Steve Broadbent

Over the next decade electronics will revolutionise the capabilities of combat aircraft. Spearheading this development will be those projects in which the customary mechanical link between the pilot and the flying control surfaces is replaced entirely by electronics. Before investigating just what fly-by-wire (FBW), as

Fly-by-wire Active Control Technology Jaguar (right) in company with conventionally controlled Tornado F2 prototype. Note the maximum negative lift position of the highly stable Tornado's tailplane, compared with the slight positive lift being generated by that of the deliberately unstable Jaguar. *(BAe)*

this technique is called, will offer both designer and pilot, let us first examine what happens today in a conventional attack aircraft.

Imagine that you are the pilot of a high-speed combat aircraft — an RAF Jaguar, for example. You are patrolling at low level, looking for ground targets while always keeping more than one eye open for enemy fighters. Your Jaguar is a single-seater, so you're in complete command of all the systems as well as the flying of the aircraft. The instruments tell you that you are at 3,000ft and flying at 450kt, about 520mph.

Suddenly you spot an enemy tank convoy just off the starboard wing. The formation leader tells you to attack and you pull hard into a right-hand descending turn: stick slightly to the right, then well back, pulling perhaps 4-5g in the turn, advancing the throttles and diving on the target. Weapons selected, lined up on the target and at perhaps 200ft and 550kt (635mph) you fire the guns or rockets. Then it's a hard climbing turn with full power, weaving to avoid enemy ground fire, all the time watching out for attacking aircraft, and now also looking to rejoin your formation.

It's been a hectic 90 seconds, with a host of switches to be set, decisions to be made and all the flight parameters (airspeed, height, g, angle of attack) to monitor continuously. But what exactly happened when you pulled back on the stick to start the attack run? Attached to the base of the control column are metal rods which run the full length of the aircraft to the spoilers, located on the wing for roll control, and to the all-moving tailplane, for pitch control. Just before reaching the tailplane and spoilers the rods feed into hydraulically powered jacks which amplify the force of the pilot's pull on the stick and move the flying surfaces against the tremendous air loads.

The system is entirely mechanical: whatever the pilot demands — the harder or farther back he pulls the stick — he gets in terms of deflection of the tailplane, which in turn causes the nose to pitch upwards. Too hard a pull and the Jaguar can enter a catastrophic stall or spin, or the maximum g limit can be exceeded and the aircraft damaged. In the excitement of attacking a target, when every ounce of performance is needed from aircraft and crew, it is very easy for the pilot to make a handling mistake and crash. With so much else to watch for, a dangerously high angle-of-attack reading can go unnoticed, and there is nothing in a mechanical system, save for one or two simple warning lights, to keep the pilot from disaster if his own vigilance fails him. Too shallow a turn and he may miss the target or fall into the sights of the enemy; too tight a turn and the aircraft can become uncontrollable and crash. In combat the difference between success and failure is small.

What then if we replace the mechanical rods with electronics, leaving everything else the same? A useful weight saving is the most obvious result, with electrical cables replacing the bulky rods and, since no mechanical leverage is required with an electronic system, a small sidestick supplanting the control column. But the main advantage of installing FBW is the fact that the pilot can now be protected from spinning and overstressing the aircraft by the computer which lies at the heart of the electronic system.

Although FBW has been around for many years — an experimental aircraft flew with an FBW system for one pilot and a mechanical back-up for the other as early as 1957 — it is only recently that the necessary electronics have become reliable enough to permit elimination of mechanical back-up in a combat aircraft. The computers must be extremely fast and powerful, and the electronic wiring to the flying control actuators must be duplicated so that the aircraft remains controllable even if one line is damaged. The wiring must also be completely proof against interference from any of the aircraft's other electrical signals. Even now, so great is the concern with reliability that Britain's first totally FBW aircraft, an experimental Jaguar developed jointly by British Aerospace and GEC Avionics, carries no fewer than four computers to make absolutely sure that the system is as safe as a mechanical one.

Let's return now to our combat sortie, this time in an FBW Jaguar. Pull into the attack manoeuvre once more. The computer senses your demand for a tight turn with maximum g, and commands just enough control-surface movement — and no more. You are fully protected from spinning and overstressing, and you can go into an attack knowing that the aircraft's maximum safe performance will be at your disposal. This in turn means that you can pay more attention to getting the switches set and hitting the target first time, again with the help of a computer. The attack is safer and more effective.

It is reckoned that the cost of installing FBW in existing aircraft like the Jaguar would be more than covered by the consequent reduction in the number of aircraft lost in training as a result of handling errors. Though increased combat effectiveness is harder to quantify, it must amount to a large proportion of an air force's budget, equivalent to many millions of pounds. But the benefits of FBW go further still, and to understand this we must first look at some basic aerodynamic theory.

In a conventional aircraft the lift created by the wing acts at a point *behind* the aircraft's centre of gravity, and to balance the machine in straight-and-level flight the

ACT Jaguar seen during early FBW trials, before the application of the destabilising wing-root strakes. *(BAe)*

The first destabilising strake has been fitted, while the port wing root has been stripped in readiness for the second. *(BAe)*

tailplane generates a *downward* force. This arrangement is stable: if a small force (eg a gust of wind or turbulence) causes the aircraft to deviate from the straight and level, it will tend to return quickly to its original attitude. The further behind the centre of gravity (cg) the centre of lift (known as centre of pressure or cp) is located, the more stable the aircraft. Move the cg well foward of the cp and the aircraft becomes very stable and almost impossible to manoeuvre. Close the gap and stability is reduced until, as the two points nearly coincide, the aircraft is so unstable that the pilot finds it increasingly difficult to control the pitch attitude and is fighting a losing battle against the effects of small disturbances.

Eventually, when the cp is *ahead* of the cg, the aircraft is completely unstable and even the smallest disturbance will lead to an uncontrollable divergence: without the aid of a computer the pilot simply cannot

react fast enough to smooth out the motion. This condition is known as "relaxed stability". The trials Jaguar has been made so unstable that a disturbance in pitch of just one quarter of a degree would normally lead to the aircraft exceeding its limits in well under two seconds. Yet the aircraft flies beautifully. How is this achieved?

The fly-by-wire computer takes in data from sensors which detect the aircraft's speed, attitude, altitude and a whole lot more, and monitors any slight change. If a disturbance in pitch is felt, the tailplane is ordered to correct for it so quickly that the pilot is unaware of it and has a smooth flight. Many times every second the computer calculates the exact tailplane angle needed to keep the aircraft in the attitude being demanded by the pilot, and signals the tailplane jacks to make the required very small changes to tailplane angle. So FBW gives the pilot two big benefits: carefree handling — he is protected from stalling, spinning and overstressing — and the ability to fly without difficulty an aircraft that is unstable.

But why should he want to fly an unstable aircraft?

ACT Jaguar's first take-off in its new, highly unstable condition. The strakes move the centre of lift forward, reducing longitudinal stability by about 10%. *(BAe)*

After all, every current combat aircraft is carefully designed so that the cg is just the right distance ahead of the cp to yield the required degree of stability, which in turn results in acceptable characteristics in every phase of flight. (The cp moves fore and aft with change of speed, while the cg shifts as bombs are released or fuel used, for example. The distance between the two can thus vary significantly during a flight, but in a conventional aircraft must never become either so big or so small that flying qualities are unacceptable, although there will always be a compromise at the extremes.) Well, if the lift goes ahead of the weight, resulting in instability, then instead of producing a downwards force to balance the aircraft, the tailplane must create an upwards force, or lift. Since an aircraft needs only a specific amount of lift to fly, the tailplane's contribution can be deducted from the lift otherwise needed from the wing, which can thus be made smaller and lighter.

In practice it has been found that the tailplane will contribute enough lift to allow the wing to be made one-tenth smaller than it would be in a stable aircraft. The smaller the wing, the tighter the turning circle, improving combat effectiveness. Again, a smaller wing means a lighter aircraft, and therefore a smaller engine for the same performance and less fuel for a given mission. A smaller, lighter aircraft is not only more manoeuvrable and harder for the enemy to see and attack, but is also cheaper to build. An air force can have a larger number of more capable aircraft for the same money. There are other benefits too. Compared with a stable aircraft, an unstable type needs only very small tailplane deflections, which means that the tailplane can be made one-third smaller. Apart from saving weight, this also reduces drag, which means that the aircraft will fly and accelerate better. Relaxed stability also results in valuable drag reductions in supersonic flight, thereby improving endurance and acceleration in this important regime.

So, FBW gives the pilot complete protection against stalling, spinning and overstressing. It allows him to make maximum-performance turns, and increases the turning capability. Aircraft weight, drag and cost all decrease for a given mission, while speed, acceleration and manoeuvrability all improve. Everyone benefits, so where's the catch? Only that until recently it was impossible to make computers fast, accurate and reliable enough to ensure that FBW types were at least as safe to fly as a conventionally stable aircraft with mechanical controls. But now the problems have been solved, and several combat aircraft are appearing with fly-by-wire and an unstable configuration.

The first all-FBW aircraft to become operational were the General Dynamics F-16 in America and the Dassault Mirage 2000 in France. However, both use analogue computing, which has long since been overtaken in effectiveness in this type of application by digital technologies. Many F-16s are now to be retrofitted with a Bendix digital FBW system developed under the Advanced Fighter Technology Integration (AFTI) programme, in which a modified F-16 first flew in July 1982.

The world's first fully operational all-FBW aircraft, the F-16 also features relaxed stability and automatic variable wing camber.

Having pioneered FBW with the Avro 707 in 1957, Britain has since 1977 devoted much effort to a national programme centred on the Jaguar mentioned above. This aircraft completed about 80 flights between October 1981 and October 1984 and is now stored pending the development of the next generation of equipment. Aim of the programme is an advanced FBW system for the proposed European Fighter Aircraft (EFA), which is due to fly at the end of the decade, and the Jaguar demonstrator will probably be fitted with a new system for trials towards the end of 1985. The Experimental Aircraft Programme (EAP) demonstrator, also being developed by British Aerospace at Warton, will fly in spring 1986 with the new system, which by then will have been proven on extensive ground rigs as well as on the Jaguar.

There are another two projects aimed at keeping Britain in the forefront of this technology. At Cranfield College of Aeronautics a Hawk and a Harrier are being converted into FBW aircraft. Two-seaters, they will both have FBW in one cockpit — the Hawk in the front and the Harrier in the rear — while the other crew member, with conventional mechanical flying controls, will act as safety pilot.

Top: **Astra Hawk's FBW system will give trainee test pilots a taste of a wide variety of handling characteristics.**

Above: **The VAAC Harrier is pioneering the use of FBW to reduce the demands on the pilot, particularly during the tricky transition between vertical and horizontal flight.**

The Hawk programme is known as Astra (Advanced System Training Aircraft). The aircraft is due to fly at the beginning of 1986, and when trials and evaluation are completed the Hawk will be used for pilot training by the Empire Test Pilots School at Boscombe Down. The student test pilot in the front seat will be able to experience a wide range of flight characteristics, with the rear-seat instructor using his control panel to reprogram the FBW system in order to change the stability level, for example, or make the Hawk handle like another type. Should the student exceed specified flight limitations, his FBW system will be disconnected automatically and control will revert to the instructor.

The Harrier, from the Royal Aircraft Establishment at Bedford, will be used by the RAE to investigate the use of modern flight control systems in vertical take-off and landing techniques, and the front cockpit will also have electronically signalled throttle and nozzle controls. Like the Astra Hawk, the Vectored Thrust Aircraft Advanced Flight Control (VAAC) Harrier is currently undergoing extensive avionics modifications and should also fly early in 1986.

Several other combat aircraft now being designed around the world, notably the Swedish JAS 39 Gripen and the Israeli Lavi, incorporate FBW systems with no mechanical back-up. Both of these aircraft will fully

Grumman X-29 forward-swept-wing research aircraft pictured during its maiden flight, on December 14, 1984. FBW makes it possible to exploit to the full the aerodynamic advantages of this configuration. *(Grumman)*

exploit FBW by being basically unstable. Taking combat aircraft design yet another step forward is a research aircraft which made its first flight in America at the end of 1984.

The Grumman X-29 incorporates digital FBW and a number of other new and emerging technologies, the most obvious being the forward-swept wing (FSW). This concept is not new, having first been demonstrated in Germany in 1944, but only since the development of carbon-fibre materials has it been possible to make a wing strong enough for this application. For although FSW gives better low-speed handling, higher manoeuvrability and less tendency to spin when compared with a conventional aft-swept wing, it also generates twisting forces that would destroy a metal structure. It has been estimated that FSW can give 20-25% more performance than an aft-swept design.

Add to this the benefits of FBW, and the jump in performance from today's operational aircraft to those of the year 2000 will be dramatic indeed. The X-29 is leading the way to those new designs.

Where next? FBW will become established in more and more military aircraft as the principle of no mechanical back-up gains acceptance and computers continue to grow in power and reliability. The wires themselves may well be replaced by fibre-optics, in which light rather than electrical signals is used to transmit the information. Such systems are proof against any form of electronic interference and therefore offer safety improvements without any weight penalty. Fly-by-light is following hard on the heels of FBW, the main challenge being the development of fibres capable of withstanding the physical demands of military operations, and that is not a big task compared with the progress made so far on the computing side. FSW and other unstable configurations will become the norm in combat aircraft design, and the fighters being designed in the year 2000 will be as different physically from today's aircraft as today's are from those of the 1950s.

Electric Raven lands in Europe

Martin Streetly

On July 1, 1983, US Air Force Europe (USAFE) formally activated the 42nd Electronic Combat Squadron (ECS) as part of the 20th Tactical Fighter Wing (TFW) at RAF Upper Heyford. The squadron received its first aircraft eight months later, in February 1984. The formation of this unit was a major milestone in an 18-month programme designed to introduce the Grumman EF-111A Raven to the European theatre.

This major new electronic warfare (EW) aircraft is the result of studies in the late 1960s of a tactical EW system to replace the USAF's ageing EB-66s. Until 1968 this work had centred on extending the life of the EB-66 by updating its EW suite and fitting new wings and engines to improve flight performance. But then it was realised that such an aircraft would be unable to meet the demands of current and expected combat environments, especially in Europe.

The next possibility, considered between 1968 and 1970, was a purchase of the US Navy's Grumman EA-6B Prowler/AN/ALQ-99 tactical jamming system (TJS). Both the airframe and the jamming suite were well proven production items, but the Air Force concluded that the former offered insufficient performance and range. The ALQ-99 suite was however considered more than satisfactory, and it was decided to install the system in a high-performance type capable of opera-

tions in concert with the Air Force's major tactical strike aircraft. Surplus F-111A airframes were chosen for the programme, and Grumman, with its experience on the EA-6B and the ill-fated naval F-111B, was given the job of converting the type into a dedicated EW platform.

Initially Grumman was not at all sure that the project was possible. In the Prowler the ALQ-99 requires three operators, and it was clearly impossible to house that many plus a pilot in the two-seat F-111 without a major redesign of the forward fuselage or a reduction in internal fuel capacity, neither of which was acceptable to the Air Force.

The programme was saved by the appearance of the ICAP model of the ALQ-99 during 1974. This variant was so highly automated that it could be used by a single operator and therefore installed in an essentially unaltered F-111 airframe. The new model, designated ALQ-99E and developed between 1974 and 1978, is the heart of the production EF-111A.

The emergence of ALQ-99E cleared the way for full-scale airframe development, and in January 1975 Grumman was awarded an $85.9 million contract for

Heading picture: **Grumman EF-111A Raven, AF serial 66-0056, of the 42nd ECS.** *(USAF)*

161

The EF-111A's ventral canoe radome runs the length of the weapons bay, starting just aft of the nose undercarriage. *(USAF)*

the construction of two prototype EF-111s. These aircraft were in fact preceded by an F-111A fitted with a ventral "canoe" radome of the type proposed for production examples. This was used to check the aerodynamics of the installation, while five static airframes underwent a series of electronic tests. The first aerodynamically representative prototype (AF serial 66-0049) made its maiden flight on March 10, 1977. Together with the second aircraft (66-0041), which carried a complete electronic suite, it took part in an 84-flight company test programme and an 86-flight evaluation by the Air Force.

Full-scale production of the EF-111A was approved in November 1979 and the two prototypes were reworked to definitive standard. 049 reappeared on June 19, 1981, and was initially retained by Grumman for further testing, while 041 became the first "production" aircraft to be delivered to the Air Force.

The EF-111 programme calls for the conversion of 42 aircraft, including the two reworked prototypes, from existing F-111As. Production is currently divided into six lots, with 049 comprising Lot I, and 041 and one other Lot II. There are four aircraft in Lot III, eight in Lot IV, 12 in Lot V and 15 in Lot VI. All Lot I, II and III aircraft were delivered during 1982, with the Lot IV machines appearing by late summer 1983. Lot V aircraft were due to be completed by September

1984, with the final 15 aircraft being delivered at monthly intervals between that date and November 1985.

Despite appearances, the EF-111A is a virtual rebuild of the original aircraft. During the conversion Grumman removes the wings and tail surfaces and strips the fuselage back to the keel structure. When the rebuild is complete the original components have a fatigue life of about 8,000hr, while the new features are cleared for 10,000hr. This is considered enough for a peacetime service life of about 30 years.

The forward avionics bay remains unchanged and continues to house the AN/APQ-160 navigation and AN/APQ-110 terrain-following radars which are standard to the F-111A. Aft of the radar boxes, a new oxygen converter has been installed along with a large quantity of classified electronic equipment.

The crew escape capsule is retained, the right-hand side of the cockpit being completely rebuilt to house an electronic warfare officer (EWO) and his controls. Apart from some additions and rearrangement the pilot's instrumentation remains essentially similar to that of the original aircraft.

Aft of the cockpit, the weapon bay has been extensively reworked to house the transmission and other elements of the ALQ-99. The installation takes the form of a pallet hung along the bay, with nine transmitters attached to its underside and a range of related electronics above.

Completing the weapon-bay modifications is the

4.9m-long canoe radome for the ALQ-99's transmission antenna; the radome is built into the underside of the bay doors. The electronics pallet weighs 1,939kg and the canoe a further 210kg, giving a total installation weight of 2,149kg. To provide power for the system the original 60kVA engine-mounted generators have been replaced with 90kVA units. This increase in power necessitated a new electrical subsystem and extensive rewiring.

Two new environmental control systems have been installed to cope with the heat output of the palletised ALQ-99: the air cycling system from the F-111F and a refrigeration system giving a constant 4.4°C airflow for electronics cooling. The air cycling unit has a ram air intake below the starboard main engine inlet duct and two exhausts mounted on either side of the rear of the underfuselage canoe. The refrigeration system incorporates heat-exchangers mounted in reconfigured tailplane root fairings.

The fin has been restressed to carry a tip fairing and four side blisters housing a Systems Integrated Receiver (SIR) group, which provides threat data. The fin-top pod is produced by Canadair and weighs 432kg fully equipped. An integral glove fairs the installation into the fin. The standard F-111A vent tank and HF antenna are retained within the fin.

Navigation and traffic control systems comprise the APQ-110 and APQ-160 radars plus the AN/AJQ-20A inertial navigation system (INS), AN/APN-167 radar altimeter, AN/ARN-58 instrument landing system (ILS), AN/ARA-50 UHF direction-finder, AN/ARN-118(V) TACAN and AN/APX-64 IFF.

Communications equipment comprises the AN/ARC-164 UHF and AN/ARC-112 HF radios and AN/AIC-25 crew interphone unit. The defensive EW suite is composed of the AN/ALQ-137(V)4 continuous-wave deception jammer, AN/ALR-62(V)4 threat warning receiver, AN/ALE-28 chaff dispenser and AN/ALR-23 infra-red warning receiver. (The last-named is not in use on the 42nd ECS's aircraft, though the control panel and space for the installation are retained.) The offensive EW equipment is the ALQ-99E TJS, which in the EF-111A is believed to generate modulated jamming over the VHF/UHF to J-band range in six system-specific steps. Nine of the system's transmitters, covering the system-specific bands 4, 5/6, 7, 8 and 9, are housed on the weapon-bay pallet, while that for Bands 1/2 is located elsewhere.

Dimensions of the EF-111A differ little from those of the F-111A, with a span of 19.20m fully spread and 9.74m fully swept, length of 23.16m and height of 6.10m. Power is provided by the original TF30-P-3 twin-spool turbofans rated at 82.3kN with afterburning, and there is provision for 14,515kg of JP-4 fuel internally, carried in forward and aft fuselage tanks and wet wings. There is provision for in-flight refuelling. The wing pylons sometimes seen on these aircraft are

The EF-111A's fin has been restressed to carry the SIR-group antenna. Clearly visible is the blanked-off housing for the AN/ALR-23 receiver at the rear of the fin-top pod. The two bodies running alongside the afterburners house the rear-facing transmission/reception aerials for the AN/ALQ-137. *(USAF)*

used not for drop tanks but for the luggage pods carried during deployments.

The EF-111A has an empty weight of 25,855kg, rising to 40,824kg for a normal take-off. Estimated performance includes a maximum combat speed of 2,216km/hr, service ceiling of 13,715m, ferry range on internal fuel of 3,706km, unrefuelled endurance of more than four hours, and, depending on role, an average combat speed of 595-940km/hr and a combat radius of 370-1,495km.

The EF-111A Raven is intended to provide EW support for NATO's strike aircraft by countering hos-

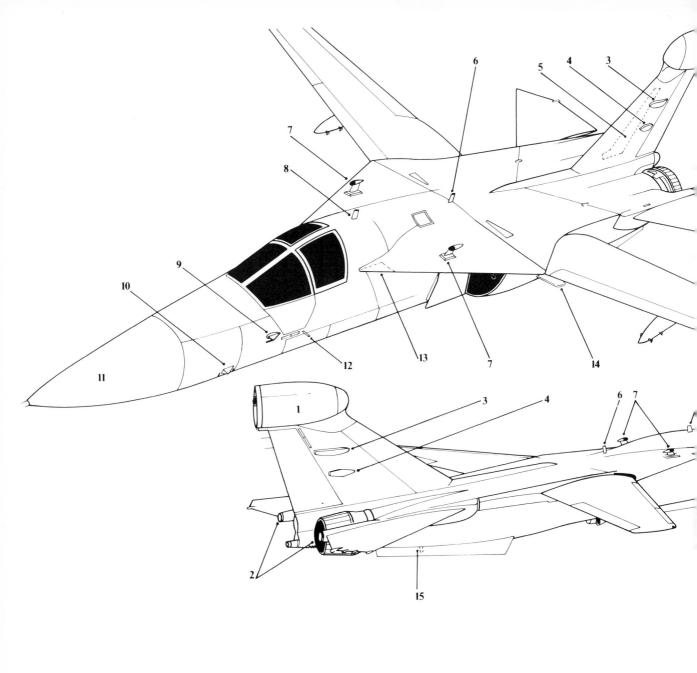

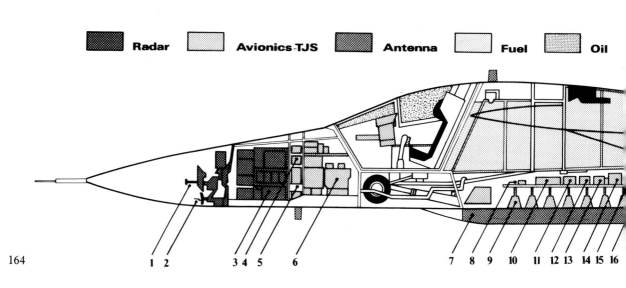

Radar ▓ Avionics-TJS ▒ Antenna ▓ Fuel ▢ Oil ▒

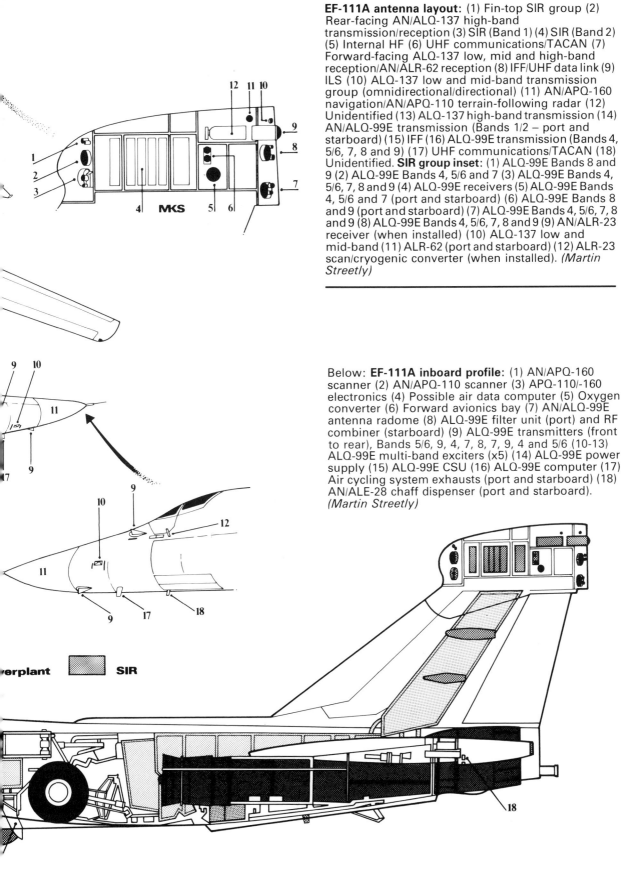

EF-111A antenna layout: (1) Fin-top SIR group (2) Rear-facing AN/ALQ-137 high-band transmission/reception (3) SIR (Band 1) (4) SIR (Band 2) (5) Internal HF (6) UHF communications/TACAN (7) Forward-facing ALQ-137 low, mid and high-band reception/AN/ALR-62 reception (8) IFF/UHF data link (9) ILS (10) ALQ-137 low and mid-band transmission group (omnidirectional/directional) (11) AN/APQ-160 navigation/AN/APQ-110 terrain-following radar (12) Unidentified (13) ALQ-137 high-band transmission (14) AN/ALQ-99E transmission (Bands 1/2 – port and starboard) (15) IFF (16) ALQ-99E transmission (Bands 4, 5/6, 7, 8 and 9) (17) UHF communications/TACAN (18) Unidentified. **SIR group inset:** (1) ALQ-99E Bands 8 and 9 (2) ALQ-99E Bands 4, 5/6 and 7 (3) ALQ-99E Bands 4, 5/6, 7, 8 and 9 (4) ALQ-99E receivers (5) ALQ-99E Bands 4, 5/6 and 7 (port and starboard) (6) ALQ-99E Bands 8 and 9 (port and starboard) (7) ALQ-99E Bands 4, 5/6, 7, 8 and 9 (8) ALQ-99E Bands 4, 5/6, 7, 8 and 9 (9) AN/ALR-23 receiver (when installed) (10) ALQ-137 low and mid-band (11) ALR-62 (port and starboard) (12) ALR-23 scan/cryogenic converter (when installed). *(Martin Streetly)*

Below: **EF-111A inboard profile:** (1) AN/APQ-160 scanner (2) AN/APQ-110 scanner (3) APQ-110/-160 electronics (4) Possible air data computer (5) Oxygen converter (6) Forward avionics bay (7) AN/ALQ-99E antenna radome (8) ALQ-99E filter unit (port) and RF combiner (starboard) (9) ALQ-99E transmitters (front to rear), Bands 5/6, 9, 4, 7, 8, 7, 9, 4 and 5/6 (10-13) ALQ-99E multi-band exciters (x5) (14) ALQ-99E power supply (15) ALQ-99E CSU (16) ALQ-99E computer (17) Air cycling system exhausts (port and starboard) (18) AN/ALE-28 chaff dispenser (port and starboard). *(Martin Streetly)*

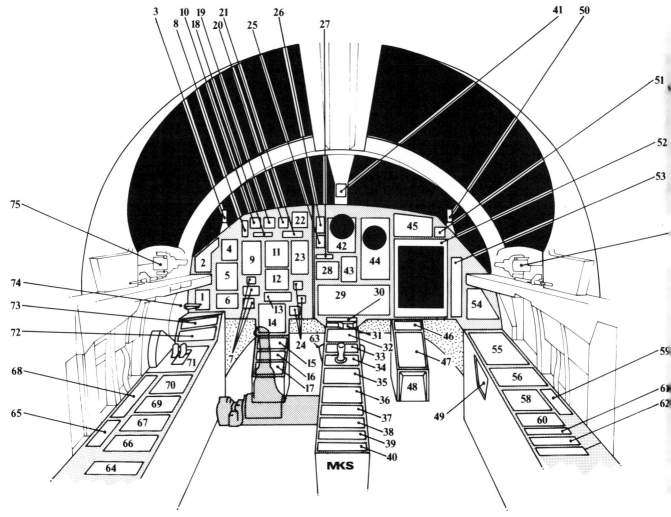

Cockpit layout

(1) Landing gear control panel (2) External stores jettison, fire extinguisher /alarm test, and fuselage/engine fire warning lights (3) Angle of attack index (4) Wing sweep indicator (5) Tachometers and turbine inlet temperature/fuel flow indicators (6) Engine nozzle position/engine pressure ratio indicators (7) Hydraulic pressure/control surface position indicators (8) Pilot's threat indicator (9) Airspeed indicator (10) Reserve airspeed indicator (11) Attitude director/indicator (12) Horizontal situation indicator (13) Landing gear position indicators (14) Caution lamp panel (15) Caution lamp panel (16) AN/ALR-23 control panel (installed but not currently in use) (17) Ram doors/oil quantity panels (18) Left status panel (19) Attitude indicator (20) Standby vertical velocity indicator (21) Right status panel (22) Radar altimeter indicator (23) Attitude/vertical velocity indicators (24) Fuselage fuel quantity/total selective fuel quantity indicators and tank selection control (25) Standby altimeter (26) Hydraulic pressure caution indicators (27) Master caution lamp (28) UHF radio control panel (29) Inertial computer unit control panel (30) Stores jettison selection panel (31) Landing gear emergency release (32) Fuel control panel (33) AN/APQ-110 control panel (34) AN/APQ-160 slew panel (35) AN/APQ-160 control panel (36) IFF control panel (37) TACAN control panel (38) Electrical control panel (39) ILS control panel (40) Air-conditioning control panel (41) Standby magnetic compass (42) AN/APQ-110 scope (43) AN/ALR-62 control panel (44) AN/APQ-160 scope (45) AN/ALQ-137 warning panel (46) Disposables control panel (47) Digital display indicator control panel (48) Storage bag (49) Internal lighting circuit-breaker (50) Angle of attack index (51) Clock (52) Digital display indicator (53) AN/ALQ-99E status panel (54) AN/ALQ-99E mode selection panel (55) AN/ALQ-99E control panel (56) SIR group control panel (57) Canopy latch (58) AN/ALQ-137 control panel (59) Cooling/power monitoring panel (60) Interphone control panel (61) UHF, TACAN and IFF antenna selection panel (62) Chaff/flare control panel (63) Ejection seat firing handle (64) Emergency oxygen control (65) Compass control panel (66) Windscreen wash and anti-freeze controls (67) Auxiliary flight control panel (68) Flight control test panel (69) Interphone control panel (70) Autopilot damper control (71) Throttles (72) Miscellaneous switch panel (73) Auxiliary gauge panel (74) Auxiliary brake handle (75) Canopy latch. *(Martin Streetly)*

tile early-warning, ground-controlled interception, and missile target-acquisition radars. Three types of operation are envisaged: penetration escort, stand-off jamming, and forward edge of battle area (FEBA) support. In the first, the Ravens would be integrated with strike formations, countering hostile emitters as they appeared. In the stand-off role EF-111As would operate in friendly airspace, flying "racetrack" patterns and working together to erect a general jamming barrier designed to disrupt the opposing air defence system. In the FEBA support role the aircraft would again operate in friendly airspace, supporting NATO ground attack and anti-armour aircraft by neutralising enemy surface-to-air missile radars. The US Air Force is extremely reticent about the EF-111's EW performance, but effective jamming range is said to be 231km and Grumman has claimed that five Ravens operating in the stand-off role could erect an unbroken jamming

Top: **EF-111A cockpit, showing the compact nature of the installation and the digital display screen for the AN/ALQ-99E on the far right of the main instrument panel.** *(USAF)*

Above: **EWO's side console in the EF-111A cockpit. The panel at the forward end contains the AN/ALQ-99E transmitter controls. Each transmitter has a master switch ("radiate", "standby" and "off" settings) and an operational mode selector (automatic and two manual settings).** *(USAF)*

barrier equal in length to the straight-line distance between the Baltic and the Adriatic.

The Raven achieved initial operational capability in November 1983 and is currently serving with the 390th (formerly the 388th TFS) ECS, 366th TFW, based at Mountain Home AFB, Idaho, and the 42nd ECS, 20th TFW, stationed at RAF Upper Heyford.

At full strength the 42nd ECS will have 12 aircraft and 60 personnel, including 13 flight crews. Upper Heyford's centralised servicing complex will receive an additional 225 technicians, 30-40% of whom will specialise in the systems specific to the EF-111.

Before taking up his present post 42nd ECS commanding officer Lt-Col David Vesley was EF-111 conversion manager within USAFE, a position which gave him a broad view of the aircraft's European deployment. He wants his squadron to be fully integrated with the other units at Upper Heyford: "The roles are diverse, but we're all here for the same purpose and I have a lot of concern about my squadron getting separated socially, professionally and everything else from the other units on the base."

Have there been any problems in recruiting crews for what might seem to be a second-line duty? "Initially I thought we were going to have to go out and draft and pull as hard as we could to get pilots and EWOs into the system. Surprisingly, however, we don't have a single aircrewman who has not volunteered to be in the EF-111 programme. This is one of the few aeroplanes ever to be built specifically for the EWO, and so there is a lot of interest."

Has the complexity of the EF-111 created any maintenance problems? "I've been very surprised with the maintenance of the aeroplane; it's been quite good. The problems we have run into are basically F-111 problems because it's an old airframe. In fact, most of them are the oldest As on the inventory. We have fuel leaks, mostly in the wings, which are not touched by Grumman when they're modifying the airframe. We're very satisfied so far."

After flying the F-111F Lt-Col Vesley finds the Raven underpowered. But "it flies basically like an F-111. There are very few tasks which are unfamiliar to the pilot [with F-111 experience]; there are some instruments which have been moved around and the aircraft is a little bit heavier on take-off." Overall, his impression is of a "very clean aeroplane with a heavy feel but not the dragginess created by flying with bombs under the wings."

The initial batch of 42nd ECS pilots were all F-111 qualified and had little difficulty in converting to the new model. But the specialised nature of the EWO's job has meant a redistribution of the navigational workload, which "depends on which arena of the flight you are in. If we are in a low-level environment, where the demands are really on flying the aeroplane and keeping from hitting the ground, the right-hander reverts to being a standard navigator and the pilot flies the aeroplane. When you get into a higher environment, where the EWOs are now primarily orientated towards the ALQ-99, then the pilot picks up the navigational responsibilities." Low-level operations are simplified by the EF-111A's terrain-following capability, which remains the same as that of the F-111A.

In day-to-day training Lt-Col Vesley emphasises "those areas which are more demanding and critical in flight. For example, the low-level function is something that an EF-111 in wartime probably isn't going to do nearly as much as an F-111. But I put a high priority

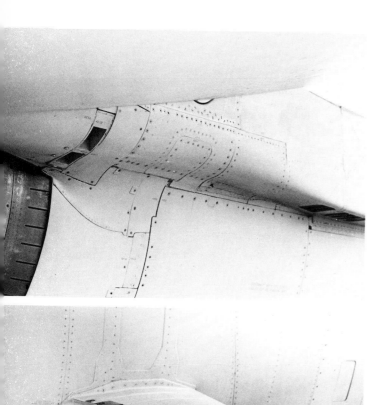

The reconfigured tailplane root fairing, with AN/ALE-28 chaff chutes. These fairings also house the heat-exchangers for the AN/ALQ-99E refrigeration unit. (USAF)

on the training involved in low-level work because that's the most demanding and where I have got to have the guys as efficient as possible. We try to do low-level work on most missions, weather permitting. However, most of our work is going to be done at middle to high altitudes, and even for the penetration escort role our time at low level is not going to be all that great. Another aspect that we try to work on very hard is orbit or airspace management. You're going to be in a compact area, you're going to have to counter the defences while you're in there doing your job, and that requires the separation of duties between the right and left-seater. So we've got to work at that."

Is the powerful ALQ-99 ever switched on inside British airspace? "Yes, though obviously under very strict rules, primarily from the host nation in which we are flying. In other words, we go to the MoD here to clear operational sorties. In fact, they were knocking on our door at an early stage, asking us to employ the aircraft against the UK's air defences. But we have to be very careful about this because if we don't follow the rules we can cause problems with civilian radars. All of the missions have very strict rules for peacetime employment of electronic jamming of any sort. We live very strictly by these rules because if we don't we're going to lose our training opportunities."

How effective would the 42nd ECS be in war? "It depends on the conflict, on what you can afford and how to balance the demands against what you are able to do. My 12 aeroplanes are not going to be the panacea for any World War III conflict that's going to go on. I'd love to have more aircraft." There are no current plans to reinforce the 42nd ECS in times of crisis, though the US-based 390th TFS is deployable worldwide.

On the EW effort as a whole, Lt-Col Vesley believes that much remains to be done: "It's one aspect of combat which we just haven't put enough effort into, for one very good reason: it's darned expensive and it's difficult to afford the systems which are required. The field is absolutely critical, especially if you're going to fight out-gunned, out-manned and out-planed."

Centre: **AN/ALQ-99E transmission antenna for Bands 1 and 2.** (USAF)

Left: **One of the two ALQ-137 antennae mounted on the upper surfaces of the wing-root fillets.** (USAF)

Dassault's ageless Super Etendard

Tim Wrixon

More than a quarter-century after the original prototype first flew, France's Super Etendard naval strike fighter looks like serving on well into the 1990s. The key to the longevity of this Dassault design — which has proved in partnership with the Exocet missile to be a deadly weapon system — is a continuing series of equipment and airframe improvements.

The Super Etendard was the first French military aircraft to be equipped with an inertial nav/attack system, setting the pattern for succeeding French combat types since it entered service in 1978. When the Marine Nationale began to look for something better than the original 1950s-vintage Etendard, a naval version of the Jaguar was the first choice, but this was cancelled in 1973. The Navy then compiled a long list of improvements which would turn the Etendard into a first-class weapon system. The main modifications affected the engine, airframe and, particularly, the avionics. The Super Etendard needed a really good radar for ship strikes, and the Thomson-CSF Agave lightweight search/track/designation/telemetry navigation radar was chosen. The Sagem-Kearfott ETNA inertial navigation and attack system was the other major innovation, and the aircraft also incorporated a Thompson-CSF VE-120 head-up display.

The Super Etendard was originally seen as essentially the same as the Etendard IVM except for the new nav/attack system, but by the time the Navy had specified a more powerful and economical engine, improved aerodynamics and other new equipment, the Super Etendard was at least 90% a new aeroplane. A total of 100 production Super Etendards were to have been built, but this was cut to 71 by budget economies. The Argentinian Navy then placed an order for 14 in 1979, making a total of 85. Of the French Navy order,

Heading picture: **A French Navy Super Etendard is catapulted from the carrier** Clemenceau.

169

A French Navy Super Etendard armed with Exocet missile. *(Dassault)*

five were diverted to the Iraqi Air Force; these are due to be returned to Dassault for refurbishment in about a year. The French Navy has three squadrons, each with about 15 aircraft, so about 21 aircraft are in reserve or have been the victims of what is claimed to be a modest attrition rate.

Although all the jigs and tools are still available it is unlikely that the Super Etendard will be put back into production. All 85 had been completed by the end of 1983. Dassault is however keeping its options open in case a customer should come along with a requirement for a reasonable number, and the type is still promoted during military export sales campaigns. There is always the possibility, too, that the French Navy will re-order the remaining 29 aircraft of its original requirement. The 71 built under the budget restrictions were originally thought to be too few, but fortunately there have been very few accidents. So unless a crisis arises, it looks as if the Navy will be happy to bide its time until the introduction of the ACM (the maritime version of the *Avion de Combat Tactique*), which will operate from the new PAN-1 nuclear aircraft carriers from about 1995.

Meanwhile, the existing Super Etendard airframe is seen as suitable for continued operational service, provided that updated avionics are fitted. The Navy is looking at developments of the Exocet ASM and the new Matra AAM, the Armat, which the aircraft might be able to carry. The admirals also want to improve the aircraft's ECM and ECCM capabilities. The performance of the airframe is becoming increasingly subordinate to that of the avionics and weapons, and the Super Etendard could well continue in service in updated form for its full life of up to 20 years.

It has been suggested that a reconnaissance version

of the Super Etendard might be developed. What is more likely is that a camera pack will replace the two DEFA 30mm cannon at present located in the underside of the engine air intakes. Now that Magic AAMs can be carried on the wing pylons, the photo-reconnaissance Super Etendard would have no need of cannon for self-defence.

The French Navy is likely to continue flying its original Etendard IVMs and Etendard IVPs, the former for ground attack and the latter for photo-reconnaissance, into the beginning of the 1990s. The Etendard IVM first went into service in 1962, so a remarkably long service life is being foreseen for these aircraft. Again, this has been made possible by the adoption of new avionics, basically an inertial nav/attack system and head-up display. These modifications were due for completion by mid-1985.

The Super Etendard inherited a rugged airframe from the Etendard IVM. Accessibility and ease of maintenance were built into the design, as was a high standard of aerodynamic finish. The airframe and attachments are stressed to an ultimate load factor of 12g and a limiting load factor of 8.6g. The maritime environment is highly corrosive, so special attention has been paid to protective treatments, including chromic anodising and protective paint for aluminium alloys, epoxy paint for high-tensile steels, and polyurethane paint for the finishing colours.

The Super Etendard nose section includes the radar, inertial navigation unit, radar altimeter and retractable in-flight refuelling probe. The centre fuselage includes the pressurised cockpit, the electronics equipment bay (for communications and the air-data computer), the air intake ducts, internal fuel tanks, airbrakes, gun pack, arrester hook, tail attachments and one attachment point for external stores. The rear fuselage is detachable at a transport joint for engine removal.

The wing's box-type major assembly forms an integral fuel tank. Wing-to-fuselage attachment is of the multi-bolt type, and the high-lift devices include drooping leading edges and double-slotted flaps. Both ailerons and spoilers are fitted, and other features include folding tips and two attachment points for external stores.

The fin is in two parts, the lower being integral with the fuselage. The rudder is hinged to the upper fin, and the horizontal stabiliser pitch trim is automatically linked to flap position. The undercarriage has been designed to absorb carrier landing loads, and the nose gear is equipped with a shock-absorber overpressure setting to cater for catapult operations.

Super Etendards carrying 1,100lit external tanks.

The single, non-afterburning SNECMA Atar 8K50 turbojet delivers a maximum thrust of 5,000kg. It can be started from the aircraft battery and features an electronic jetpipe temperature corrector. Simple access and removal was a design requirement. Total internal fuel capacity is 3,270lit, plus another 2,800lit in external tanks. The internal tanks are divided into separate halves for safety reasons. Other fuel system equipment includes the retractable flight-refuelling probe, facilities for fast ground pressure refuelling, and a dump valve.

Flying control surfaces consist of the horizontal stabiliser (for pitch control and damping), ailerons and spoilers for roll control, rudder, high-lift devices (including drooping leading edges and double-slotted flaps), and airbrakes under the fuselage. The horizontal stabilisers, ailerons and spoilers, rudder and drooping leading edges are controlled through the fail-safe hydraulic system, which incorporates twin-ram servo jacks fed by two entirely separate circuits. The double-slotted flaps and associated pitch trim are each actuated

by twin electric motors, and the airbrakes are driven by single-barrel hydraulic actuators.

Super Etendard maintainability is high: minimum turnround time is 20min, and fewer than 11 man-hours of work are needed for every flight hour. Ground handling equipment is reduced to a minimum by the aircraft's built-in test equipment and self-starting system. Pressure refuelling of both internal and external tanks can be completed in a total of eight minutes. An engine change can be achieved in only two hours by three engineers, and gun reloading is facilitated by exchangeable ammunition boxes. Ground handling equipment is fully air-transportable.

When fitted with the optional refuelling pod and control system the Super Etendard can both take on fuel in flight and refuel other aircraft. The tanker aircraft can transfer all the fuel from its pylon and internal tanks, except for a reserve of 300kg, while a receiver Super Etendard can fill its pylon tanks and take 1,355kg into its internal tanks.

The Super Etendard is armed with two DEFA 552A 30mm guns firing at a rate of 1,250 rounds per minute, both guns and shells being located in a quickly removable pack. Externally, the aircraft can carry two Matra 550 Magic infra-red missiles, two to six 250kg clean or retarded bombs, two to four 400kg clean or retarded bombs, two to four LR150 rocket launchers, or one long-range air-to-surface missile. Various combinations are possible. The fire-control system comprises a VE120 CRT head-up display, an Agave multi-role radar, and the Sagem inertial digital/analogue high-precision nav/attack system.

A Super Etendard on the catapult aboard the carrier *Clemenceau.*

Communications are provided by a TRT/ERA UHF set, Socrat VHF set and EMD IFF transponder. There is a Crouzet air-data computer, an LMT Tacan receiver, Socrat VOR/ILS, and TRT radar altimeter. The radar warning system is by Thomson-CSF.

Wing span of the Super Etendard is 9.60m (7.80m folded), length 14.31m and height 3.85m. Wing area is 28.4m². Thickness/chord ratio varies from 5 to 6% and leading-edge sweep is 47° 53′. Take-off weight of the clean aircraft is 9,450kg, empty weight 6,500kg. Maximum speed at low altitude is 1,205km/hr and close to Mach 1 at 10,000m. Stabilised ceiling is 14,600m. Maximum steady turn rate at sea level is 15°/sec, and sustained load factor is 6g, also at sea level.

On a typical hi-hi air-superiority mission the Super Etendard would have a combat radius of 1,200km, carrying two external tanks dropped before combat. In this configuration it would be armed with two Matra 550 missiles in addition to the guns. For a lo-lo air-superiority sortie the combat radius would be 540km with two external tanks dropped before combat. The armament would be the same as for the hi-hi mission. A hi-lo-hi attack mission, the aircraft could carry two 400kg bombs over a radius of 700km. Alternatively, carrying one Exocet ASM, one 600lit tank and one of 1,100lit, it would have a radius of 880km. In the lo-lo-lo attack case, with one Exocet and the same drop tanks, it would have a radius of 545km. In the last two cases buddy refuelling could be used to increase the radius of action.

Commuterliner cornucopia

J. M. Ramsden

Dornier 228-200. *(Dornier)*

No fewer than 30 types of aircraft are on offer to the regional airlines of the world. The commuterlines, as they are sometimes called, are rich in choice if not in pocket, and their favours are being courted by 19 international aircraft manufacturers. Nine of these are in production with completely new designs, and their ardour is exceeded only by their anxiety that the commuterliner market may not be big enough for all.

This most competitive international airline sector operates passenger aircraft seating from 10 to 70. All are propeller-driven, most by turbines. Those in the light category have been developed from general-aviation business and utility aircraft. Those in the large category, with 40-70 seats in pressurised cabins and costing $8 million-$9 million each, incorporate the advanced technology of the major airliner and civil aero-engine manufacturers.

Nobody has yet made a jet economic enough to compete on short routes of up to 500km. Although the BAe 146, Boeing 737, Fokker F.28 and F100 and the McDonnell Douglas DC-9/MD80 series overlap the commuterline networks, they are too big, fast and expensive to be considered for this market.

A commuterliner was once defined as a transport aircraft weighing not more than 5,700kg and with fewer than 20 passenger seats. As the regional airlines

grew and the market demanded more capacity, the definition extended to 40 passengers and a maximum weight without fuel of 16,000kg. Now the industry is being offered 60-seaters like the BAe 748ATP and the Fokker 50, which weigh more than 20 tonnes gross.

These aircraft are typical of the "heavy" commuterliners, of which there are eight on offer. They are outnumbered by the types in the light and medium categories, defined as aircraft with fewer than 20 seats and 20-40 seats respectively.

Light commuterliners (10-20 seats)
Antonov PZL Mielec An-28 Poland's PZL Mielec manufactures the Soviet-designed Antonov An-28, bearer of the best known name in Russian light transport aircraft. The An-28 has been described as the Soviet Union's Twin Otter. Hundreds are in operation throughout the socialist republics, and a few have been exported to other countries. The 20-seat An-28 is powered by two Glushenkov 960hp turboprops. The aircraft has been steadily improved since the prototype flew in 1973.
Beechcraft Airliner and King Air America's most successful business turboprop, the King Air and family has bred three distinct types of commuterliner.

The 13-seat Super King Air/B200 is powered by two

Beechcraft Super King Air 300.

850hp Pratt & Whitney Canada PT6A turboprops. It has a pressurised cabin and a range of more than 1,200km at a useful cruising speed of 450km/hr. Price is $1.87 million. Latest Super King Air model is the B300 at $2.34 million, carrying the same payload faster over a longer range.

The Beech C99 Commuter flew for the first time in 1980, eight years after the Super King Air, and was aimed specifically at the commuterline market. Seating 15 passengers in pressurised comfort, the C99 (160 built) has been superseded on the production line by the 1900 Airliner. Powered by uprated PT6A turboprops, this 1982 model seats up to 19 and has more tankage and range. It can have a big door for cargo work, and costs $2.85 million.

British Aerospace Jetstream 31 Built by the Scottish Division of British Aerospace, the 18-seat pressurised twin-Garrett TPE331 Jetstream 31 has been notching up orders throughout the recession, and is proving particularly successful in the American and European commuterline markets. It looks and is fast, with a "big aerospace technology" background derived from British Aerospace experience with Airbus, BAe 146 and Concorde.

BAe Jetstream 31 in the colours of West German commuter operator Contactair.

Cessna Caravan I and II America's leading manufacturer of light aircraft is offering two types of light commuterliner, Caravan I and Caravan II. They are quite different aircraft, despite their common name. Caravan I is a utility single, Caravan II a business twin. Both are powered by the PT6A.

Caravan I has seating for 12 passengers, or 13 for the single-pilot operations usual in the utility business. It has big doors for cargo as standard, and has been winning orders well in a generally weak market. The aircraft could well be a modern successor to the classic piston-engined Beaver and single Otter. Though a single lacks twin-engined performance and safety, the 600hp PT6A-114 is extremely reliable and offers gains in economy and maintenance cost. For operators who do not have to fly over long stretches of water or at night, the single-engined Caravan, first flown in 1982, could have a long run ahead of it in competition with the more expensive twins. Price is $650,000.

Caravan II is being offered in co-operation with Cessna's long-established European partner, Reims of France. The aircraft is being built under licence as a development of the highly successful range of Cessna business twins, which includes the 402C Utililiner, 421 Golden Eagle and Conquest. It seats 12 passengers. Though the market is still slow, the Reims production line has been set up in anticipation of an improvement.

de Havilland Canada Twin Otter 300 More than 800 Twin Otters have been built since the first one flew in 1965. The Series 300 is the latest model of this light commuterliner classic. No aircraft can claim to be tougher or more versatile. It is in service in 74 countries, and in military as well as civil roles. Most are 20-seat mini-airliners, but many are used full-time as freighters. Power is provided by two 620hp Pratt & Whitney Canada PT6As and price is US$2.1 million.

Dornier 228-200 This 19-seater twin Garrett TPE331-powered product of West Germany's aerospace industry has evolved from the successful Dornier Skyservant. The 228 has a new-technology wing and a bigger fuselage (a slightly shorter version, the 228-100, seats 15).

More than 40 228s have been delivered into the sort of rough, tough environments with which the Skyservant has coped so well. The Indian Government, after a long comparative evaluation, has taken a licence through the state-owned Hindustan Aircraft to build 228s in Kanpur. The initial deal covers 150 aircraft, the first eight of which will be made from Dornier-supplied kits. The aircraft will be used by Indian regional operators as well as by the air force, navy and coastguard. India will be allowed to market the 228 in those areas where it has better contacts than Dornier.

Fairchild Metro III This is one of a number of US business twins which took the short step to a commuterliner version. Developed from the Merlin III, the 20-seat twin-Garrett TPE331 Metro III also comes with

PT6A engines, when it is designated Metro IIIA. The two versions are in commuterline service with a dozen US and European carriers, and Fairchild's experience has benefited the larger new commuterliner being made in partnership with Sweden's Saab, the Saab-Fairchild 340 (see below).

GAF (Australia) Nomad N24A Production of the 16-seat twin-Allison 250B Nomad has finished, but half a dozen commuterliner versions are available new at a price of US$1.2 million. More than 100 of the 172 aircraft built are civil, of which 30 are in commuterline use (Nomad 24As).

Harbin Turbo-Panda Promotion of this Chinese Twin Otter copy has slackened in the last year, and arrangements for the aircraft to be marketed by a British distributor have been postponed. The prototype of this 17-seater flew in 1981. It is powered by Pratt & Whitney Canada PT6As. Demand for this type of aircraft in China must be vast, and there seems little doubt that the country's ambitious and competent aerospace industry will make a technical success of it.

LET L-410UVP Turbolet This 15-seat turboprop twin (730hp Czech Walters) is the product and design of Czechoslovakia's able and independent aerospace industry, the national aircraft section of which is known as LET. The Turbolet has become standard equipment with Aeroflot, which uses it on commuterline and industrial operations all over the Soviet Union. About 500 are reported to have been built.

Pilatus Britten-Norman Islander Britain's best-selling transport aircraft — 1,000-plus built in all versions and still in production — is the Islander. About 30 a year have been delivered right through the recession, half of them turbine-powered with Allison 250Cs in place of the original Avco Lycoming 540 piston engines. The Turbine Islander has the same seating — 10 including crew — and the same design profile: the most efficient, simple and tough light transport aircraft that aerospace and transport experience, and low manufacturing costs, could produce. The Islander has always been built by small factories, and the current sole source is Romania's aerospace industry in Bucharest, with completion by Pilatus Britten-Norman in the Isle of Wight, England. Price of the Turbine Islander is $730,000.

Pilatus, the Swiss parent, also has in production a capable light single turboprop, the 10-seat Turbo Porter.

Piper Chieftain One of the first names which springs to mind at the mention of the word "commuterliner" is the Piper Chieftain, of which about 500 are in service — so successfully, both in America and abroad, that the Piper Corporation decided to set up a specialised Airline Division. The Chieftain is another commuterliner to have evolved from a business twin, in this case the popular Navajo.

A turboprop version of the 10-seat Chieftain, with one more seat, is designated T-1040; the price goes up from $460,000 to $870,000, for which the customer gets more payload, range and speed.

Shorts Skyvan This boxy 19-seater with its useful rear-loading cargo doors is powered by two Garrett TPE331s and is now in its 22nd year of production. More than 150 have been delivered. The Skyvan has led to the more passenger-conscious Shorts 330 and 360 (see below) and to a freighter version of the 330 designated Sherpa. Skyvan costs $1.2 million.

Medium commuterliners (20-40 seats)

Casa 212 Aviocar The Casa 212 is probably the closest aircraft to the irreplaceable DC-3. About the same in capacity, seating 28, this twin-Garrett TPE331 product of Spain's aerospace industry has a rear-loading cargo fuselage, a feature unique in its class. More than 400 have been sold all over the world. Price is $2.4 million. Casa and Indonesia's Nurtanio are jointly making a bigger development, the CN-235 (see below).

de Havilland Canada Dash 8 This is the latest member of the successful Canadian family of light transports. Powered by Canada's new-generation PW120 turboprop, the 36-seat short take-off and landing (Stol) type is now entering service, backed despite the recession by a good order book. Price is US$5.2 million.

Embraer EMB-110 Bandeirante and 120 Brasilia Brazil's successful Bandeirante 20-seat commuterliner is in service with 70 operators in 23 countries, and more than 400 have been built, half for export.

Encouraged by this success, the Brazilians have moved upmarket with a more refined and bigger successor, the Brasilia, a 30-seater powered by new-generation PW115 turboprops of 1,590hp. It cruises at 500km/hr and is pressurised. Price is $4.7 million, including electronic flight instrument displays.

US-registered Embraer EMB-110 Bandeirante.

Shorts 360s destined for service with Simmons Airlines (Michigan, USA) and on the Allegheny Commuter network. *(Shorts)*

Saab-Fairchild 340 Sweden's highly successful but mainly military aerospace industry has gone into partnership with America's very experienced builder of commuterliners and business twins (FH-227, Metro, Merlin). The result, now in service, is the 34-seat pressurised 340 powered by new-generation 1,700hp GE CT7 turboprops. It has a new-technology flight instrument system and built-in test equipment to cut maintenance costs. The 340 is the first of the new-era commuterliners to enter service (1984). Price: $5.3 million.

Shorts 330 and 360 These well established low-cost British commuterliners have as their biggest passenger attraction stand-up cabin headroom and ample galley, baggage and lavatory space. The 30-seat 330 costs $3.3 million and the 36-seat 360 $4 million. Shorts has delivered a combined total of more than 150 and despite the recession is building and selling them at a rate of three a month.

Large commuterliners (40-70 seats)
Aérospatiale-Aeritalia ATR42-200 This joint effort by the French and Italian airframe industries is a new-technology aircraft powered by new-generation PW120 turboprops of 1,800hp. Pressurised and with an electronic cockpit and auto-maintenance systems, it has been on test since summer 1984 and should enter service this year (1985). Price is $6.5 million. A stretched version to seat 60 is planned.
Antonov An-26 Flying since 1968, this reliable Russian is the heaviest of the heavies, with rear loading for cargo work. The cabin can seat 40. Hundreds are in Aeroflot service, powered by two Ivchenko turboprops.
British Aerospace 748 and 748ATP The BAe 748 is one of the world's most successful commuterliners, still

in production after a quarter century and more than 350 built. The latest model has the 536-series version of Rolls-Royce's legendary Dart turboprop, and 48 seats four-abreast in a pressurised cabin. Price is $6 million.

Building on the 748's success, BAe has decided to develop a completely new and bigger (64 seats) Advanced Turboprop (ATP) powered by new-generation PW124 engines. It has an electronic cockpit and all the latest automatic maintenance features, while retaining the best of the proven 748 structure. Price: $8.8 million.
Casa-Nurtanio CN-235 The aerospace industries of Spain and Indonesia, already partners in production of the successful 212 (see above), have decided to develop a bigger (44-seat) aircraft with the unusual amenities of big aft "garage" doors and pressurisation. This ambitious aircraft could be needed in hundreds for the Indonesian market alone. Price is $4.9 million, including new-era GE CT7 turboprops and electronic cockpit, making the CN-235 the cheapest of the new-technology types.
de Havilland Canada Dash 7 The Canadian manufacturer is the only one with a model in each commuterliner category. The heavy is the four-engined (PT6A) Dash 7, with 50 seats and the best short-field performance in its class. Into it has been gone all the experience acquired with Twin Otter. The prototype first flew ten years ago, and more than 100 are in service. Price: US$5.9 million.
Fokker F.27 and F50 The F.27 Friendship is Europe's most successful airliner, with more than 700 built. Fokker is building on the success of this Dart-powered 52-seater with the new-technology F50, which combines all the good features of the F.27 with new engines (PW124s) and electronic cockpit. Price: $8 million.